毕淑敏
双语美文

A Bilingual Edition of
Beautiful Stories
by Bi Shumin

爱的回音壁

Love's Echo Shall Ring

毕淑敏 著

朱虹 刘海明 译

GUANGXI NORMAL UNIVERSITY PRESS

广西师范大学出版社

·桂林·

爱的回音壁
AI DE HUIYINBI

出版统筹：张俊显
品牌总监：耿　磊
选题策划：耿　磊
责任编辑：王芝楠
助理编辑：韩杰文
美术编辑：卜翠红　刘冬敏
营销编辑：杜文心　钟小文
责任技编：李春林

图书在版编目（CIP）数据

　　爱的回音壁：汉、英 / 毕淑敏著；朱虹，刘海明译. —
桂林：广西师范大学出版社，2020.1
　　（毕淑敏双语美文）
　　ISBN 978-7-5598-2395-3

　　Ⅰ. ①爱… Ⅱ. ①毕…②朱…③刘… Ⅲ. ①散文集－
中国－当代－汉、英 Ⅳ. ①I267

　　中国版本图书馆 CIP 数据核字（2019）第 259732 号

广西师范大学出版社出版发行
（广西桂林市五里店路 9 号　邮政编码：541004）
网址：http://www.bbtpress.com
出版人：黄轩庄
全国新华书店经销
保定市中画美凯印刷有限公司印刷
（保定市西三环 1566 号　邮政编码：071000）
开本：880 mm × 1 350 mm　1/32
印张：6　　字数：120 千字
2020 年 1 月第 1 版　　2020 年 1 月第 1 次印刷
印数：0 001~6 000 册　　定价：39.80 元

如发现印装质量问题，影响阅读，请与出版社发行部门联系调换。

在书中温暖相遇

　　几年前，广西师范大学出版社出版了我的一套书。在这套书里，我写了自己在遥远西藏的往事，写了当医生的难忘经历，写了担当心理医生时听到的故事和引发的思考……

　　书是缔造心灵的塑形工具。东方文化中，心并不单单指那个解剖学上的泵血器官，而是汇聚每个人的品格情操的智慧之海。有一颗仁慈之心，会爱世界爱他人爱生活，爱自身也爱大家。有一颗自强之心，会勤学苦练百折不挠，宠辱不惊大智若愚。有一颗尊严之心，会珍惜自然善待万物。有一颗流量充沛羽翼丰满的心，会乘上幻想飞船，抚摸众星的翅膀。

　　我遇到了朱虹老师，她就是拥有这样一颗多彩之心的睿智长者。很高兴她喜欢我书中的文字。

　　最初，朱虹老师想挑一些篇章翻译，作为礼物送给远在大洋彼岸的孙女外孙女们珍藏。广西师大出版社的编辑获悉这个想法，郑重邀请朱虹和刘海明老师，将本套书全部翻译出来。

　　这不是轻易可完成之事，是颇为繁复艰辛的工程。朱虹老师已年近90，是中国社科院德高望重的英美文学研究专家，也是一位把我国很多当代文学作品翻译介绍到国外的杰出翻译家。长期生活在国外的刘海明老师造诣高超文采斐然，和朱虹老师相得益彰珠联璧合。两位老师以醇厚学养和丰富经验，深思熟虑地将这些文字，按照英语思维方式和阅读风格，给予精彩转化，赋予它们以另外一种语言表达的鲜活生命。

补充一个小插曲。我的散文"精神的三间小屋"，被选入2018年教育部审定的全国义务教育语文教科书九年级上册。刘海明老师加班加点，将这篇文章翻译出来，收入本套书，真是雪中送炭。

面对这套双语书，我心中充盈知遇之恩和感念之情，在此向所有付出心血的老师们深表谢意！

人生是砥砺向前且充满顿挫的历程，不时筋疲力尽茫然四顾。这本小书的故事和它的成书过程，让我又一次相信，行程中有不期而至的风雨，更有美好温暖的巧遇。朱虹、海明老师和我在文字中结识，现在，我期待着——我们和你——亲爱的读者，在书中相逢。

之后，让咱们再次充满信心地出发！

2019年11月5日

When We Meet Inside a Book

A few years ago, Guangxi Normal University Press published a collection of my stories. In them, I wrote about the years I spent in remote Tibet, my unforgettable experience working as a physician, and stories and musings I gathered as a counseling psychologist.

Works of literature help shape our heart. In Eastern cultures, the heart is the sea of wisdom that nurtures our character, other than a mere organ anatomically responsible for pumping blood through the body. It is with the kind heart that one loves the world, others and life; love of oneself and all people. It is with the hardy, aspiring heart that one strives on, never giving up, and is wise, artless and unflappable. It is with the dignified heart that one cherishes nature and is kind to all creatures great and small. It is with the heart brimful of confidence that one floats on wings of imagination, touching the stars.

Then I met Zhu Hong, an erudite elder with such an unfailingly rich heart, and was most delighted that she liked the stories of this collection.

Initially, Zhu Hong had planned to translate a selection of them as a gift to be held dear by her granddaughters across the ocean. However, when the editorial staff of Guangxi Normal University Press learned about this, they decided to invite Zhu Hong and Liu Haiming to translate the entire collection into English.

It was no small undertaking, a project requiring much dedication. Zhu Hong, in her late eighties, is a venerated scholar in the field of English and American Literature with the Chinese Academy of Social Sciences. She is also noted for her incomparable translations of outstanding works of modern Chinese literature, bringing them to a wider international audience. Liu Haiming, an accomplished translator having studied and worked extensively abroad, collaborated with Zhu Hong on this project. The two scholar-translators pored over the Chinese texts and managed to bring out the spirit of the original, and give life to the stories in the English language in all its beauty and flexibility.

Incidentally, my essay "Three Little 'Rooms' for Your Soul" was selected for the 2018 edition of the Ministry of Education-approved high school textbook for Chinese Language and Literature, for the first semester of the ninth year of National Compulsory Education. Beavering away, Liu Haiming had it timely translated for inclusion in the present collection.

As this bilingual collection was ready for printing, I felt most grateful for our privileged connection. My thanks go to all who have put all the hard work into its publication.

Life is a journey, with inevitable challenges and setbacks, which, at times, can wear you out, and loneliness captures you. Yet, for all the storms out of the blue, there are also fortuitous, heartening encounters along the way—a belief borne out by the stories in this collection and its publication. Zhu Hong, Haiming and I met in the pages of these stories, and now I look forward to our encounter with you, dear readers, in this little collection.

Then, brimful of confidence again, we will journey on!

Bi Shumin, November 5, 2019

contents
目 录

contents
目 录

额头与额头相贴

如今，家家都有体温表。苗条的玻璃小棒，头顶银亮的铠甲，肚子里藏一根闪烁的黑线，只在特定的角度瞬忽一闪。捻动它的时候，仿佛打开裹着幽灵的咒纸，病了或者没病，高烧还是低烧，就在焦灼的眼神中现出答案。

小时家中有一支精致的体温表，银头，好似一粒扁杏仁。它装在一支粗糙的黑色钢笔套里。我看过一部反特小说，说情报就是藏在没有尖儿的钢笔里，那个套就更有几分神秘。

妈妈把体温表收藏在我家最小的抽屉——缝纫

机的抽屉里。妈妈平日上班极忙，很少有工夫动针线，那里就是家中最稳妥的所在。

七八岁的我，对天地万物都好奇得恨不能放到嘴里尝一尝。我跳皮筋回来，经过镜子，偶然看到我的脸红得像在炉膛里烧好可以夹到冷炉子里去引火的炭。我想，我一定发烧了，觉得自己的脸可以把一盆冷水烧开，我决定给自己测量一下体温。

我拧开黑色钢笔套，体温表像定时炸弹一样安静。我很利索地把它夹在腋下，冰冷如蛇的凉意从腋下直抵肋骨。我耐心地等待了五分钟，这是妈妈惯常守候的时间。

终于到了。我小心翼翼地拿出来，像妈妈一样眯起双眼把它对着太阳晃动。

我什么也没看到，体温表如同一条宁澈的小溪，鱼呀虾呀一概没有。

我百般不解，难道我已成了冷血动物，体温表根本不屑于告诉我了吗？

对啦！妈妈每次给我夹表前，都要把表狠狠甩几下，仿佛上面沾满了水珠。一定是我忘了这一关键操作，体温表才表示缄默。

我拈起体温表，全力甩去。我听到背后发出犹如檐下冰凌折断般的清脆响声。回头一看，体温表的"扁杏仁"裂成了无数亮白珠子，在地面轻盈地溅动……

罪魁是缝纫机板锐利的折角。

怎么办呀？

妈妈非常珍爱这支体温表，不是因为贵重，而是因为稀少。那时候，水银似乎是军用品，极少用于寻常百姓，体温表就成为一种奢侈。楼上楼下的邻居都来借用这支体温表，每个人拿走它时都说："请放心，绝不会打碎。"

现在，它碎了，碎尸万段。我知道，任何修复它的可能都是痴心妄想。

我望着窗棂发呆，看着它们由灼亮的柏油样棕色转为暗淡的树根样棕黑色。

我祈祷自己发烧，高高地烧。我知道，妈妈对得病的孩子格外怜爱，我宁愿用自身的痛苦赎回罪孽。

妈妈回来了。

我默不作声。我把那只空钢笔套摆在最显眼的地方，希望妈妈主动发现它。我坚持认为被别人察觉错误比自报家门要少些恐怖，表示我愿意接受任何惩罚，而不是凭自首减轻责任。

妈妈忙着做饭。我的心越发沉重，仿佛装满水银（我已经知道水银很沉重，丢失了水银头的体温表轻飘得像支秃笔）。

实在等待不下去了，我就飞快地走到妈妈跟前，大声说，我把体温表打碎了！

每当我遇到害怕的事情，我就迎头跑过去，好像迫不及待的样子。

妈妈把我狠狠地打了一顿。

那支体温表消失了，它在我的感情里留下一个黑洞。潜意识里我恨我的母亲——她对我太不宽容！谁还没失手打碎过东西？我亲眼看见她打碎了一只很美丽的碗，随手把两片碗碴儿一撂，丢到垃圾堆里完事。

大人和小人，是如此不平等啊！

不久，我病了。我像被人塞到老太太裹着白棉被的冰棍箱里，从骨头缝里往外散发寒气。妈妈，我冷。我说。

你可能发烧了。妈妈说，伸手去拉缝纫机的小屉，但手臂随即僵在半空。

妈妈用手抚摸我的头。她的手很凉，指甲周旁有几根小毛刺，把我的额头刮得很痛。

我刚回来，手太凉，不知你究竟烧得怎样，要不要赶快去医院……妈妈拼命搓着手指。

妈妈俯下身，用她的唇来吻我的额头，以试探我的温度。

母亲是严厉的人。从我有记忆以来，从未吻过我们。这一次，因为我的过失，她吻了我。那一刻，我心中充满感动。

妈妈的口唇有一种菊花的味道，那时她患很严重的贫血，一直在吃中药。她的唇很干热，像外壳坚硬内瓤却很柔软的果子。

可是，妈妈还是无法断定我的热度。她扶住我的头，轻轻地把她的额头与我的额头相贴。她的每一只眼睛看定我的每一只眼睛，因为距离太近，我看不到她的脸庞全部，只感到一片灼热的苍白。她的额头像碾子似的滚过，用每一寸肌肤感受我的温度，自言自语，这么烫，可别抽风……

我终于知道了我的错误的严重性。

后来，弟弟妹妹也有过类似的情形。我默然不语，妈妈也不再提起，但体温表像树一样栽在心中。

终于，我看到了许多许多支体温表。那一瞬，我的脸上肯定灌满了贪婪。

我当了卫生兵，每天须给病人查体温。体温表插在盛满消毒液的盘子里，好像一位老人生日蛋糕上的银蜡烛。

多想拿走一支还给妈妈呀！可医院的体温表虽多，管理也很严格。纵使打碎了，原价赔偿，也得将那破损的尸骸附上，方予补发。我每天对着成堆的体温表处心积虑、摩拳擦掌，就是无法搞到一支。

后来，我做了化验员，离体温表更遥远了。一天，部队军马所来求援，说军马们得了莫名其妙的怪症，他们的化验员恰好不在，希望人医们伸出友谊之手。老化验员对我说，你去吧！都是高原上的性命，不容易。人兽同理。"

一匹砂红色的军马立在四根木桩内，马耳像竹笋般立着，双眼皮的大眼睛贮满泪水，好像随时会跪倒。我以为要从毛茸茸的马耳朵上抽血，战战兢兢地不敢上前。

兽医们从马的静脉里抽出暗紫色的血。我认真检验，周到地写出报告。

我至今不知道那些马得的是什么病，只知道我的化验结果起了至关重要的作用。

兽医们很感激，说要送我两筒水果罐头作为酬劳。在维生素匮乏的高原，这不啻一粒金瓜子。我再三推辞，他们再四坚持。想起"人兽同理"，我说，那就送我一支体温表吧！

他们慨然允诺。

春草绿的塑料外壳，粗大若小手电。玻璃棒如同一根透明铅笔，所有的刻码都是洋红色的，极为清晰。

准吗？我问。毕竟这是兽用品。

很准。他们肯定地告诉我。

我珍爱地用手绢包起。本来想钉只小木匣，立时寄给妈妈，又恐关山重重、雪路迢迢，在路上震断，毁了我的苦心，于是耐着性子等到了一个士兵的第一次休假。

妈妈，你看！我高擎着那支体温表，好像它是透明的火炬。

那一刻，我还了一个愿。它像一只苍鹰，在我心中盘桓了十几年。

妈妈仔细端详着体温表说，这上面的最高刻度可测到46摄氏度，要是人，恐怕早就不行了。

我说，只要准就行了呗！

妈妈说，有了它总比没有好。只是，现在不很需要了，因为你们都已长大了……

Let Me Feel Your Forehead

Nowadays, the clinical thermometer is a household item. A glass tube with a shiny metallic crown and a hidden mercury column, could be read only when you hold it at a certain angle. To see it clearly, you may have to roll it slightly, as if unfurling a scroll of magical spell. We know the person is ill and his temperature abnormal when concern is written all over the face of the tube-holder.

Back in my time, such an exquisite instrument was a rarity and I was intrigued by the one we had at home. It had a silvery tip, like a little metal kernel, and was placed in the barrel of an old black fountain pen, which made it all the more titillating. For such a nib-less fountain pen was where intelligence could be stored in and passed on secretly, according to a spy novel I had read.

Mother kept it in the smallest drawer — that on the treadle sewing machine — in our home. As she was always busy with work, the sewing machine was rarely used and its drawer the safest place to keep things.

As a seven-year-old, I was insanely curious about everything. One day, after playing Chinese jump rope outside, I noted, as I passed in front of the mirror coming back in, that my face flushed and felt like embers, hot enough to bring a pot of water to a boil. I thought to myself I must be running a fever and should take my temperature.

I took the cap off the fountain pen barrel. The glass tube nestled snugly like a time bomb. I stuck it — cold as the skin of a snake — in my armpit, feeling its chill in the ribcage. Patiently I waited for five minutes, as mother always did, before I gingerly removed it from my armpit and, squinting, held it up against the light.

Nothing! The glass tube was blank, no hint of mercury, absolutely void, like a quiet brook without life in it.

I was puzzled. Did I just turn cold-blooded so the thermometer couldn't show any reading?

Then it occurred to me that before sticking it into my armpit, mother always gave the thermometer a few downward shakes as if to shake off any remnant water. Perhaps there's the rub! I thought.

So I took up the thermometer and shook it as hard as I could. All I heard was something smashing on the floor behind me, as if an icicle hanging off the eave crashed down to the ground. The mercury in the kernel-shaped tip broke into numerous tiny silvery beads, rolling around on the floor as if weightlessly floating.

The culprit was the hard corner of the sewing machine cabinet.

Now what do I do?

The thermometer was something very precious to mother, not because of its monetary value but it was hard to come by in those days. Mercury seemed to be restricted for military use and was rarely seen as a household item. Having a thermometer at home was a real luxury. Neighbours on other floors in the apartment building would come to borrow it, always with the promise — We will take care not to break it.

Yet, I had smashed it, breaking it into smithereens, with absolutely no chance for repair. That much I knew.

I stared blankly at the window; its grid frame, with a tawny sheen of old paint, blurring into a dim web of gnarly roots.

I prayed I be really sick, with a high fever; knowing mother would be gentle to her sick daughter. I prayed for redemption through bodily suffering.

When mother came back, I kept mute; the

empty fountain pen barrel being placed at what I thought was the most visible spot.

I hoped mother would find out by herself, which would save the agony of my confessing it. It would show that I was willing to accept any punishment for what I did, not appealing for leniency by voluntary confession.

Mother was busy making supper. My heart was heavy, as if laden with mercury. (I had learned it was a heavy substance, as the broken thermometer drained of mercury felt as light as a tiny, used brush).

The wait was more than I could bear. I went over to my mother and declared, "I broke the thermometer!"

This was typical of me. When I couldn't bear the suspenseful prospect of something dreadful, I would plunge myself into it and get it over with.

I got a sound spanking by mother.

The thermometer was gone which left a dark hole in my heart. Without knowing it, I hated mother for being unforgiving. Everyone breaks things. Who is beyond reproach?

I saw she herself once broke a very beautiful bowl. All she did was picking up the two broken halves and threw them into the bin. Such inequality between grownups and we children!

Soon afterwards, I fell ill, with shivers and feeling chilled to the bone, as if trapped in a large icebox that street hawkers used to keep popsicles from melting. "Mom, I am so cold," I moaned.

"You may have a fever," Mom said, reaching for the little drawer of the sewing machine before her hand stopped halfway.

She put her hand on my forehead. Her palm felt cold and, as it moved, a few hangnails on her fingers scratched my skin, hurting.

"Hard to tell how high your fever is, because I just came in from outside and my hands are too cold. Should we go see the doctor?" Mom said as she rubbed her fingers.

Then she stooped, her lips pressed against my

forehead to feel its temperature.

Mother was something of a disciplinarian and, as far as I could remember then, she had never kissed us before. But thanks to my little wrongdoing, she kissed me now. I felt choked up.

Mother's mouth smacked of dried chrysanthemum. She was suffering from severe anaemia and had been taking Chinese herbal medicine. Her lips felt dry but warm, like some fruit with a tough rind and soft flesh.

However, she still wasn't sure if I had a fever. She cupped my face in her hands and pressed her forehead against mine, looking me straight in the eye. With her face so close, I couldn't see it entire, but a pale, blurred contour. She rolled her forehead left and right, like the roller on the millstone, feeling each and every bit of my forehead. She muttered, "It's so hot. Pray she wouldn't get fever cramps...."

I realized what a mess I had made.

The same happened to my younger siblings when they fell ill. Mother never mentioned the thermometer again. Yet it stuck in my mind, as if having taken root like some plant.

Eventually, I would come into so many clinical thermometers. I imagine there must have been quite a look of greed when I had my first eyeful of them.

That was when I joined the army and became a medic. I was charged with the responsibility for taking the temperature of every patient in the ward. The thermometers were all put in a container, immersed in disinfectant and upright, like the numerous silvery candles on an elderly person's birthday cake.

How I wished I could take one for mother to make up for my mistake! Yet the head nurse ran a tight ship. Even though there were thermometers galore, anyone who broke one would have to pay for their misstep. A replacement would be issued only when the broken pieces were turned in. Every day, with so many thermometers at my fingertips, I itched for the chance of getting just one for myself, but to no avail.

Then I became a lab technician and the prospect became even fainter. One day, we got a request from the cavalry unit. Some of its horses were stricken with an unidentified malady. It so happened that their vet technician was away and they hoped we at the human hospital could lend a friendly hand. The senior technician said to me, "Go! Life on the highland is not easy; for humans and animals alike."

When I arrived, I saw a dun horse standing among four poles, his ears perking like bamboo shoots and large eyes brimming with tears. The horse looked as if he could give up and collapse at any moment. Assuming that blood had to be drawn from his furry ears, I hesitated in trepidation.

The vet drew some dark blood from the horse's vein. I did a careful test and filled out a thorough report.

To this day I do not know what was wrong with the horse. But I know that my test report was instrumental to the vet's diagnosis.

All the vets there were all grateful and insisted on giving me two tins of canned fruit as a reward. Knowing such vitamin-rich rations were precious and hard to come by on the highland, I declined. Yet they persisted. During the back and forth, I remembered my superior's words about humans and animals being alike. So I said, "If you insist, then give me a thermometer instead."

They were happily obliged.

It was placed in a green plastic cylinder the size of a small torchlight. The glass tube was as thick as a mechanical pencil, marked with degrees in stark red.

"Is it accurate?" I asked. After all, it was a vet thermometer.

"You bet," they said in unison.

I wrapped it carefully in my handkerchief. I thought about cobbling together a wooden box, and mailing the thermometer to mother right away

17

in the protective box. Then, I feared its destruction on the long journey over treacherous mountain passes and snowy roads. If that happened, all my efforts would come to naught. I decided to wait for my first home leave...

"Mom, look!" I held the thermometer high as if it were a torch with a crystalline stave.

I had fulfilled a promise at long last, I thought; one that I had secretly kept for over a decade, the hope for its deliverance lingering all this time, like the eagle silently hovering in the highland sky.

"Its scale tops at 46 degrees Celsius. A man would have kicked his bucket before he could ever have such a high temperature," Mom said after a careful look at the thermometer.

"As long as it is accurate, it will do, right?" I said.

"It is better than nothing, of course. Only we won't have much use for it any more. You are all grown up..." Mother sighed.

家问

家 是什么?

家会很小很小,螺蛳壳是蜗牛的家。家会很大很大,宇宙是星星的家。

家会很轻很轻,像一粒浮尘,被人一指掸掉,不留一丝痕迹。家会很重很重,像一座铅山,压在脊上,寸步难行。

家会很快乐很幸福,像一眼不老的喜泉。家会很凄楚很悲凉,像一汪深不可测的泪潭。

问年轻人,家是什么?

他们回答,家是粉红色的玫瑰,有刺更有蕾。

家是甜蜜的吻，热烈的拥抱。家是柔情似水的情话和连绵不断的短信。

问中年人，家是什么？

他们回答，家是心灵与肉体的港湾，能停泊万吨巨轮也能栖息独木小舟。家是无私的付出与接纳，家是脱去疲劳的热水澡。家是一个苹果，你一大口，我一小口。家是一副重担，我愿这边的力臂短，你那边的力臂长。

问老年人，家是什么？

他们回答，家是黄昏湖边的搀扶，家是灯下互相凝望丝丝白发。家是一件旧风衣，风也是它雨也是它。家是虽非一见钟情，却望白头偕老的漫漫旅程。家是墓前的一枝黄菊花。

问孩子，家是什么？

他们回答，家是妈妈柔软的手和爸爸宽阔的肩膀，家是一百分时的奖赏和不及格时的斥骂。家是可以耍赖撒谎当皇帝，也得俯首听命当奴隶的地方。家是既让你高飞又用一根线牵扯的风筝轴。

问情人，家是什么？

他们回答，家是舔着伤口的两只狼。家是荷尔蒙的汹涌分泌。家是一日不见，如隔三秋。家是猜忌、争执、思恋、指责的杂耍场。家是枕边泪窗前月，家是今夜你会不会来？家是一个不存在的地方。

问养家的人，家是什么？

他说，家不是勋章，你挂在胸前，别人也看不见。家是一条暗地里逼你不断挣钱的鞭子，直抽得你遍体鳞伤。

问弃家的人，家是什么？

他说，家是一种能力，一种学习。我自忖无力从那里毕业，就中途逃亡了。

问无家的人，家是什么？

他说，家是羁绊，家是约束，家是熄灭人创造激情的沼泽地，家是一种奢侈的靡费。

问恋家的人，家是什么？

他说，家是树上的喜鹊窝。纵然世界毁灭了，只要家在，依然有一切。

问恨家的人，家是什么？

他说，家是爱情的终点，家是英雄的坟墓。家是累赘，家是负担。家是挂在你项上的枷锁，家是你自卖自身的契约。

我不知世上还有另外的场所，会如此众说纷纭，褒贬不一。

纵观家庭，是大千世界的缩影。人们在家中卸去重重角色的面具，露出本色嘴脸，最坦率最赤裸。人性的善与丑，方寸之间，纤毫毕现。一代伟人，能治理好一个国，未必能调理好一个家。能统率千军万马的将军，可能是妇孺裙钗下的败将。

有人以为家是最自由最放任的所在，可以无所顾忌，百无约束。其实，家是最考验责任感的圣坛。对一个你所声称最挚爱的人，都欺瞒背叛，你还指望能为天下人所信任吗？对一个托付终身的人，都无法负起责任，你还能承诺他人的期嘱吗？连自己的一脉血缘都不能照料和抚育，你还能爱国爱民吗？在家中，我们看到了太多的丑恶。对亲人施暴的人，不可能对他人仁慈。在家中阴郁的人，不可能对太阳微笑。在家中诡计多端的人，不可能真诚地对待友人。在家中粉饰虚伪的人，不可能直面峥嵘人生。

如果没有准备好，请不要撕下走进家庭的门票。如果没有爱自己也爱他人的能力，请不要随意刨开家庭的地基。

很多人抱着从家庭中掠取支援的动机，匆匆为自己寻一个可供汲取财富和暖意的储备仓库。殊不知，家庭不是无中生有变出魔力的黑斗篷。家庭的温暖，先要无私无偿地培养和付出，然后热度才能像春草，毛茸茸地生长起来。一旦失了爱的滋养，再稳固的家也会很快风化。爱的魔力，有时很巨大，有时很贫瘠，全看你是否能以心血灌溉。

一花一世界，一家一宇宙。婴儿降临世上，家是包裹他的蛹壳。倘若家中注满健康的爱的花粉，他就吸吮着它，用爱滋养构建着自己的听觉嗅觉知觉，渐渐地酿成心中小小的蜜饯。在爱中长大的孩子，爱是他的羽衣，爱是他的长矛。在爱中蓬勃向上的孩子，他看天下，就比较明朗。他看人性，就比较乐观。他看自身，就比较有尊严。他看他人，就比较客观。他看丑恶，就比较勇敢。他看前途，就比较光明。他看事物，就比较冷静。他看死亡，就比较泰然。

在纷乱和丑恶的气氛中成长的孩子，是伪劣家庭的痛苦产品。他们在家中最先看到并习得的待人处世经验，是破碎疏离和粗暴残酷。他们是那样幼小，缺乏分辨的能力，以为这就是人世间的模型。当他们走进社会的时候，会不由自主地以不良家庭的模式对待他人，将紊乱与不协调传染到更大的范畴。更令人惊惧的是，来自不完美家庭的孩子们，彼此具有病态的吸引力，仿佛冥冥中有一块恶作剧的磁石，牵引着性格残缺的男女，使他们同病相怜，迫不及待地黏合到一处。这种建立于病态中的家庭，草台班子如履薄冰，演化成悲剧几乎是必然。如果不能进行彻底的改造，卓有成效地打断铰链，这种会伤人的家庭，就像顽强的稗草，代代相传，贻害无穷。

家可以很单纯，一个人也是一个完整的家。家可以很复杂，整个地球共居一个穹隆的屋顶。

家啊，是理解奉献思念呵护，是圣洁宽容接纳和谐，是磨合欣赏忠诚沟通，是心心相印浪漫曲折生死相依海角天涯。

What Is Home?

Home can be small; the tiny shell carried on the back of a snail. Home can be immense; the universe where stars dwell.

Home can be so insignificant; as to be easily brushed off like a speck of dust without any trace. Home can be so heavy as to weigh you down; leaden like a mountain.

Home can be a haven of peace, an ever-flowing source of joy. Home can be a dreadful abyss; a woeful tale of sorrow and despair.

Ask the young "What is home?" and they will reply—

"Home is a posy of pink roses, with spiky thorns and tender buds. Home means hugs and kisses. Home is sweet talk and the source of endless text messages."

Ask the middle-aged "What is home?" and they will reply —

"Home is the sanctuary for your body and soul; a harbour for the seafaring vessel or the lonely skiff. Home means selfless giving and accepting. Home is the hot shower when the day is done. Home is an apple to be shared — with the larger half always left by you for your other half. Home is a load that you always want to shoulder the larger share."

Ask the elderly "What is home?" and they will reply —

"Home means a lakeside stroll with your significant other at dusk; a caring look in the waning light. It is an old trench coat worn in wind and rain. It is a yearning for companionship on the long journey of aging, though no more love-at-first-sight. Home means a yellow chrysanthemum placed at the headstone year after year."

Ask a child "What is home?" and he will reply —

"Home is Mom's soft hand and Dad's broad shoulder. Home means a prize for the perfect score and a dressing-down for flunking the exam. Home is where you trick, cheat, and act like a king or obey like a slave. It is the leash that reins you in and the string that lets you fly high like a kite."

Ask a pair of lovers "What is home?" and they will reply—

"Home is where you make amends; like a pair of wolves licking wounds after a fight. Home means the rush of hormones. Home means a day feels like a thousand when being apart. Home means suspicion, quarrel, and longing. It is the blame game, the pillow talk or the blank stare on a lonely, moonlit night. It is all in the question 'Are you coming home tonight?' Home can be something you want to hide."

Ask the breadwinner "What is home?" and he will reply—

"Home is not a medal. You can't wear it on the lapel of your jacket for the world to see. Home eggs you on in your ceaseless toil; an invisible whip giving you bruises all over."

Ask the abandoner "What is home?" and he will reply —

"Home demands skills and endless learning. Seeing no hope of ever graduating, I dropped out."

Ask a vagabond "What is home?" and he will reply —

"Home is nothing but shackles. It saps your creative energy and bogs you down. It is all an extravagant waste."

Ask a family man "What is home?" and he will reply —

"Home is a nest of joy. Nothing in the world matters, as long as one has a home to come back to."

Ask the one who hates home "What is home?" and he will reply —

"As marriage is the grave of love, home is the grave of all heroic aspirations. Home is nothing but burden and encumbrance; the shackles that weigh you down and the deed that enslaves you."

Alas, such divergent views! I know no other social institution that is as divisive.

Home is after all the human world in miniature. You put down your mask at the door and are your true self at home; candid, without disguise. The good or bad in you is fully exposed. A great statesman who can run a country well may not be adept at getting his house in order. A general with battalions under his able command may fall prey to a sweet charmer.

Some believe home is where you let down your guard and lose your inhibitions. Yet, in truth, home is sacrosanct; an ultimate test of one's sense of responsibility. How can others trust you, if you cheat and betray the one you claimed to love most? How will you keep any promise, if you abandon the one who has cast her lot with you? If you don't even care for your next of kin, why should others trust your professed love for the nation? There can be much evil and ugliness in a home. He who is abusive at home will not be kind to others; he who is glum at home will not smile in the sun; he who is sly and scheming at home will not be honest to his friends; he who is pretentious and in denial at home will not face up to the challenges in life.

If you are not prepared, don't cross the threshold. If you are incapable of loving yourself and another person, you shouldn't talk about marriage.

Many rush into wedlock for what they hope to gain, as if it were a path to wealth and warmth. Little do they know home is not a magician's cape under which something is brought forth out of nothing. It takes selfless dedication to create the joy of hearth and home. It is love that makes the fire in the hearth glow. Without love, a home is doomed to crumble, no matter how solid it may seem. Love's magic depends on determined, passionate cultivation.

You see a world in a wild flower; universe in a home. Home is the cradle for the newborn, snug like a cocoon to the larva. He thrives where love glows, feeling its tenderness with all his senses and building up a reserve of love, as bees collect honey. A child brought up with love is a miracle of beauty and strength; love gives him wings to soar and the spear to be brave. Bright and joyful, he brims with confidence. Optimistic about human nature and future, he is inclined to look on the bright side and be unbiased in treating fellow humans. He is composed and clear-eyed in his assessment of any given situation; he can look at death with a touch of philosophy.

A child growing up in a family in disarray and full of animosity is an unfortunate offshoot of suffering. His earliest experience of the adult world is that of fragmentation, alienation and cruelty. Young and lacking in judgement, he takes such dysfunction for a model of life in the world at large. As he becomes an adult, he can't help treating others the way he was treated at home, projecting antagonism and discord onto the wider community. More alarmingly, children from dysfunctional homes tend to gravitate to one another. Such ill-fated attraction pulls together men and women with character flaws like a magnet. Their hasty unions, on faulty foundations, are doomed to slide to some tragic end. Without a thorough rewiring and reversal to break the cycle, families as such only pass on the suffering from one generation to the next; recurring like noxious weed season after season.

Home can be simple; a single person and a wholesome home. Home can be complex; the entire planet, humanity's only home.

Home is all about understanding, sacrifice, longing and care. It is the epitome of purity, tolerance, inclusiveness and harmony; of a deeply romantic bond strengthened in mutual appreciation and learning. Home is till death do us part. Home is within each of us, no matter how far we wander; home is always where our heart is.

当我们想家的时候

常常想家。

当我们想家的时候，其实是想起了母亲。当我们想起母亲的时候，其实是想起了无边无际、云蒸霞蔚的爱。当我们想起爱的时候，其实是想起了如天宇般宽广淳厚的温暖和一种伟大神圣的责任。当我们想起责任的时候，其实是在宁静致远地思索着人生的真谛和生命的尊严。

世上没有关于家的节日，好在有一个母亲节，让我们飘荡的心有所附着。每年这一天，人们不约而同地隆重纪念这个民间节日，感念一种饱含沧桑的爱。

最初发起为母亲设定一个节日的人，一定是一位成年的男人或女人，太小的孩子，我以为是无法理解母爱的。婴儿的热爱的涌起，更多的是源于一种生命本能的驱动。孩子从母亲那里，得到最初的食物和衣着，看到世上第一张欢颜，听到人间第一句笑语……小小的心，像一只薄而且透明的钵，盛满了乳色的爱，悄悄地涟漪着。以孩子的智力，必认为这些都是上天无缘无故倾倒的玉液琼浆，是与生俱来的赠品。

作为施与的一方，母爱有时也是本能乃至盲目愚蠢的代名词。母爱单纯也复杂，清澈也混浊，博大也狭窄，无偿也有偿。体验这种以血为缘的爱，感知它的厚重深远，纪念它的无私无畏，弘扬它的旗幡，播撒它的甘霖，需要灵敏的悟力和细腻的柔情。世人只知给予艰难，其实接受也非易事，需要虚怀若谷的智慧。只有容纳得多，才有可能付出得多。对于早年无爱的生命来说，就像没有河溪汇入的干涸之库，无法想见在旱魃猖獗时会有泉眼喷涌。

母亲于是成了一种象征。

她是低垂的五谷，她是无尽的蚕丝，她是冬天的羽毛和夏天的流萤。她是河岸的绿柳依依，她是麦田的白雪皑皑。她是永不熄灭的炉火，她是不肯降下毫厘的期望标杆。她是成绩单上的一枚签名，她是风雨中代人受过的老墙。她是记忆中永恒年轻的剪影，她是飓风中无可撼动、水波不兴的风眼。

母爱并不仅仅从生育这一生理过程中得来，它是心灵的产物。生育只是母爱的土壤，它可以贫瘠也可以富饶，可以繁衍灵芝也可滋生稗草。

我愿把人类那种最崇高而洁净的挚爱，无论来自男女，统称为母爱。

母爱如盐。盐主要是来自大海，母爱最主要的蕴含地，当然是母亲了。但世上还有湖盐、井盐、岩盐、池盐……母爱并不是母亲的专利，它是人类所有最美好、最无私、最博大的爱的总命名。比如，未生育的女子也会富含母爱，像医家泰斗林巧稚大夫，她的双手，便是摆渡万婴安达人世的慈航。在人类的发展史上，更有无数志士仁人，把无边的爱意和关怀倾泻人寰。那爱的纯正灼热，至今散发着炙烤肺腑的力度，促人们警醒，激人们向前。

无论我们是男人还是女人、成人还是少年，我们都曾欢欣地接受过母爱，我们也都可以成为辐射母爱的源泉。

When We Miss Home

We often find ourselves missing home.

When we miss home, it really is our mother that we miss most. When we think of our mother, it is her boundless love that comes to mind first and warms our heart; radiant like the alpenglow. When we think of love, it is the immense kindness and noble sense of responsibility that touches our heart. When we are put in mind of responsibility, we ponder, with quiet comprehension and profound insight, the meaning of life and the dignity of living.

There is no special day dedicated to home. Yet thankfully we have a Mother's Day to anchor our wandering soul. Even though it is not a statutory holiday, people around the world celebrate this special day every year, out of gratitude to the love that warms heart across all the vicissitudes of life.

The person who first proposed a special day to honour mother must have been someone who's got some years behind them. A very young person, yet to fully comprehend the immensity of mother's love, wouldn't fit the bill. An infant's love for its mother is mostly instinct, for mother is its source of food and warmth, the first smiling face it sees and the first sound of laughter it hears. Its little heart brims with yearning; pure and clear, with a milky tint. The sweet breast milk that flows naturally must have seemed to its a given; a natural blessing.

A mother's love may be instinctive, too; blind and even irrational. It can be at once simple and complex; pure and muddled; boundless and narrow; selfless and demanding. It takes unhindered understanding and subtle sensitivity to appreciate the loving bond of blood, to celebrate its profound and enveloping power, and its selfless courage, strength, glory, and munificence. Contrary to popular belief, it is equally difficult to give and accept. It takes big-hearted humility to accept. It is only when you have the largesse to accept you will have the power to give in equal measure. A childhood deprived of love renders one incapable of love; like a creek drying-up in a drought ravaged valley.

Maternal love thus means many things: the life-sustaining nourishment, the endless thread of silk spun into a cocoon, the down feather in winter, and the fireflies waving the nocturnal tapestry in summer. It is the shade of willow lining the river bank, the blanket of snow covering a wheat field, the roaring fire in the hearth, and the bar that is raised challengingly high. It is the signature needed for the school scorecard, the shoulder that bears all the burden, the silhouette etched in memory and forever young, and the eye of the storm; calm and unperturbed.

Maternal love is not only a physiological process; associated with pregnancy and childbirth, but also comes from heart and soul. The biological bond is merely the foundation, like soil to a crop, which can be fertile or barren; producing flowers of heavenly beauty or mere rampant weeds.

I am inclined to think maternal love is the holiest and purest of human love which can be from either man or woman.

Mother, of course, is the main source of motherly love. Yet just like the ocean being the main source of salt and there being, in addition, lake salt, well salt and rock salt, maternal love can also come from other sources. It is not the exclusive preserve of mothers, but a name for all the best, and the most selfless, munificent and profound of human love. Women who have never had children can be full of maternal love, too, like the renowned obstetrician the late Dr. Lin Qiaozhi. Over a career spanning decades, she had safely delivered tens of thousands of babies by hand and with dedication and motherly love. Throughout history, noble souls in their multitudes dedicated their lives to the welfare of humanity. Their love and compassion, motherly in its intensity and boundlessness, touches our heart and inspires us onward to this day.

Be we men or women, old or young, we have all been blessed by motherly love, at one time or another in our life, and can thus be givers of such love, too.

梅花催

很多人以为爱是虚无缥缈的感情，以为爱在我们的日常生活中发生的频率十分低；以为只有空虚的、细腻的、多愁善感的人才会在淋淋秋雨的晚上和袅袅薄雾的清晨，品着茶、吹着箫，玩味什么是爱；以为爱的降临必有异兆，在山水秀美之地或风花雪月之时，锅碗瓢盆、刀枪剑戟必定与爱不相关。

还有很多人以为自己不会爱，是缺乏技巧，以为爱是如烹调书和美容术一样，可以列出甲乙丙丁分类传授的手艺，以为只要记住在某种场合施爱的程序和技巧，自己在爱的修行上就会有一个本质性的转变和决定性的提高。

爱有没有方法呢？我想，肯定是有的。爱的方法重要不重要呢？我想，一定是重要的。但在爱当中，最重要的不是方法，而是你对于爱的理解和观念。

你郑重地爱，严肃地爱，欢快地爱，思索地爱，轻松地爱，真诚地爱，朴素地爱，永恒地爱，忠诚地爱，坚定地爱，勇敢地爱，机智地爱，沉稳地爱……你就会派生出无数爱的能力、爱的法宝、爱的方法、爱的经验。

爱是一棵大树。方法，是附着在枝干上的蓓蕾。

某年春节，我到江南去看梅花。走了很远的路，爬了许久的山，看到了无边无际的梅树，只是，没有梅花。

天气比往年要冷一些，在通常梅花怒放的日子，枝上只有饱满的花骨朵儿。怎么办呢？只有打道回府了。主人看我失望的样子，突然说，我有一个办法，可以让梅花瞬时开放。

我说，真的吗？你是谁？武则天吗？就算你真的是，如果梅花也学了牡丹，宁死不开，你又怎样呢？

主人笑笑说，用了我这办法，梅花是不能抵挡的。你就等着看它开放吧！

她说着，从枝上折了几朵各色蓓蕾（那时还没有现在这般的环保意识，摘花，罪过），放在手心，用热气暖着哈着，轻轻地揉搓……

奇迹真的在她的掌心缓缓地出现了。每一朵蓓蕾，好似被魔掌点击，竟在严寒中一瓣瓣地绽开，如同少女睡眼一般绽出了如丝的花蕊，舒展着身姿，在风中盛开了。

主人把花递到我手里，说，好好欣赏吧。我边看边惊讶地说，如果有一只巨掌，从空中将这梅林整体温和揉搓，顷刻间就会有花海涌动了啊！

主人说，用这法子可以让花像真的一样开放，但是——

她的"但是"还没有讲完，我已知那后面的转折是什么了。如此短暂的工夫，在我手中蓬开的花朵，就已经合拢、枯萎，那绝美的花姿如电光石火一般，飘然逝去。

怎么谢得这么快？我大惊失色。

因为这些花没有了枝干。没有枝干的花，绝不长久。主人说。

回到正题吧。单纯的爱的技术，就如同那没有枝干的蓓蕾，也许可以在强行的热力和人为的抚弄下开出细碎的小花，但它注定是短命和脆弱的。

我们珍视爱，是看重它的永恒和坚守。对于稍纵即逝的爱，我们只有叹息。

　　爱在什么时候，都是需要技术的。而且这些技术，会随着历史的进程，发展得更完善和周到。同时，我们无论在什么时候都更看重那技术之下的、深埋在雄厚土壤中的爱的须根。

　　如果你需要长久的、致密的、坚固的、稳定的爱，你就播种吧，你就学习吧，你就磨炼吧，你就锲而不舍地坚持求索吧，爱必将降临在每一个真诚地寻找它的眸子里。

Coax Plums to Bloom

Many think love is inexplicable, something that rarely happens in their mundane lives. Only the finely superfluous, soulful and sentimental, as they like to believe, would languidly agonize over love; preferably while sipping tea or fingering a vertical bamboo flute on a drizzly autumn night, or at some misty dawn. There must be unusual omens when love comes around, they'd chaff, no doubt in some beautiful and romantic milieu far removed from pots and pans, or arms and armours.

Some others would think they are too much of a novice and simply cannot get the hang of it. Love must be some knack, they lamented, to be studied in its various categories and passed down like that for haute cuisine or plastic surgery. Mastering its ABC and applying its techniques timely is a decisive step up in the fundamental progress of the greenhorn.

Yet, are there skills to be learned for love after all? The answer should be affirmative, I suppose. Are they important? Sure. Yet it is not the skills, but your heart and how you see and understand love that is the most important.

If you could love seriously, honestly and joyfully; with thought, a light heart, sincerity, simplicity, loyalty and ceaseless affection, dedication and valour, and with wit and grit, you will become a skilful lover, developing your knack, casting your spell and being a greenhorn no more.

Love is a large fruit tree and skills its buds.

During one Spring Festival, I travelled to the south of the country for the famous plum blossom. I took a long hike in the hills through groves of plum trees but I saw no blossoms.

It had been an unusually cold spring. There were only bulged buds when there should already have been riotous blossoming. There was nothing else to do but getting ready to return. Sensing my disappointment, my host declared she had a way to get the plum buds open instantly.

"Really?" I said. "Who do you think you are? Empress Wu Zetian who could order peonies to bloom for her majesty's pleasure? Even if you were, what would you do if the plums simply refused, like the Empress's stubborn peonies?"

"The plum flowers can't resist my method," my host grinned. "You just wait and see."

She nipped off a few buds of different colours as she spoke. (We were not as protective of plants as we are now; I pray for forgiveness.) She held buds in her cupped hands, blew warm air at them and rubbed them gently...

All the buds opened miraculously in her palm; their petals unfurling in the bitter cold one by one as if under some spell and their carpel filaments fluttering in the light breeze like a girl's eyelashes.

"For you to enjoy," my host said as she placed the blossoms in my hand.

"If there could be a gigantic pair of hands to warm and rub the entire grove," I said with amazed shock, "we would have a sea of blossoms!"

"This trick can make flower buds open faster, but…" my host said.

Hardly had she said her "but" when I knew what would happen. In an instant, the flowers in my palm had begun to close and wither. These little things of exquisite beauty faded like the sparks of a flint.

"How could they wither so fast!" I was taken aback.

"Because they were severed from the stems, they don't last," my host said.

Let's return to the main subject. Love with skills only is like the plum buds detached from the tree. It may be coaxed to bloom, as if with a puff of warm air and some compelling, but the fickle spectacle is bound to be fragile and short-lived.

We cherish love for its being enduring and everlasting.

We lament with a sigh when it is capricious and fleeting.

In whatever era, we need skills to keep a loving partnership long-lasting; skills that are evolving and can be augmented and improved upon as times change. Yet we should never neglect what true love is built upon, the important foundation that is akin to roots deep in the nourishing and stable soil.

If you are longing for a loving, enduring, strong and stable relationship, you should start planting and never cease to learn, to hone your skills and explore. Love will come around for all who search with heart.

母爱的级别

有人说，爱是与生俱来的。母爱是我们理解爱的最好范本和老师。

我以为，错。爱需要学习，需要钻研，需要切磋，需要反复实践，需要考验，需要总结经验，需要批评帮助，需要阅读，需要讨论，需要提高，需要顿悟……总之，爱是一门需要穷尽一切手段打磨和精耕细作的艺术。

与生俱来的只是动物的本能。人的爱，超越了血缘、种族、国界，它辽阔的翅膀抵达宇宙的疆界，这是地球上任何一种动物不可能天然辐射的领域。所以，爱不是如同瞳仁的颜色和身高的尺度，是一连串基因决定的先天模本，而是后天艰苦琢磨的成长之丹。

印度狼孩的故事，是一个动物母爱的典范之作。有时想，假如是一个人类的母亲，得到了一只狼的幼崽，将会怎样？一般情形下，怕是不会用乳汁哺育它长大的吧？这不但说明了母爱是盲目的，还说明如果单纯比较母爱的浓度，也许人还不如一只动物。有人会说，狼长大了，会咬人，谁敢喂它？那么，一只小鼠，就会有人类的母亲用乳汁哺育它吗？答案也基本上是否定的。

母爱并不是爱的高级阶段，因为它基本上是人类的一种本能。人类的婴儿接受母爱，是被动和无意识的。从感知者的那方面来讲，母爱首先是物质的，是生存的必要条件。如果没有母亲的乳汁和精心呵护，小婴儿根本就无法生存。所以，母爱的早期阶段是分割界限不清晰的融合，它具有母体多方面付出的照料性质，母爱的高级阶段则升华为分离和精神的构建。世上有许多母亲，可以把属于动物本能的那一部分做得较好，可以完成对子女的衣食住行的补给维护，但是对高级部分，就是超越一己、博爱人类——从血缘中弥散扩展直至升华为广博的人类之爱，未必能做到及格以至优秀。

我们不时地听到这样残酷的故事：某个母亲，因为孩子的学习成绩不好，竟把亲生骨肉殴打致残致死。这是爱吗？很多人说这不是爱，因为人们本能地拒绝承认这是爱。在大家眼中，爱是纯正和没有被任何杂质污染的，包括爱是不能有失误的。但我想，假使把那位死去的孩子复活，问他或她，你的妈妈是否爱你，我想，他或她带着满身伤痕，也许会说，妈妈爱过我……

母爱的初级阶段，常常是盲目和自怜自恋的。如果自己的童年曾经物质匮乏缺吃少穿，那么她很可能以为吃饱穿好就是爱了。如果她有未竟的理想，比如成为音乐家或是画家，那么她很可能拼命地驱赶孩子学习乐器或拿起画笔……把自己的愿望强加于人，美其名曰望子成龙、望女成凤。自己没有高等级的文凭，就希望孩子能一路读书到博士后，一洗自己的遗憾与自卑。凡此种种，普天之下俯拾皆是。多少母亲冠冕堂皇地将一己的意志，凌驾弱小孩童头上，那神圣的理由就是"爱"！天下有多少悲剧，假母爱之名上演不停。

这样的母爱，难以清晰地界定孩子是另一个完整的独立个体。这种混淆，不但是生理上的糊涂，还有更深刻的心理上的痕迹。我要说，很多成人的家庭不幸和性格缺憾，追溯起来，都和母爱只停留在低级阶段，未能完成向高级阶段的转化有关。单纯而低等级的母爱，是鱼目混珠泥沙俱下，糟粕与精华并存的原始状态。

在母爱的高级阶段，母亲要斩钉截铁高屋建瓴地完成与孩子的分隔。她高度尊重生命的不同个体之间的差异，帮助一个新的生命走向灿烂和辉煌。这种境界，即使是一个潜质优等的母亲，如果不经过修炼和学习，也是不容易天然达标的。如果将它比作一座关键的闸门，我们将忧虑地看到——无数的母亲被隔绝在门的这一边，只有经过不断学习和反思，成长优异的母亲，才能跨越这对她们自身也充满挑战的门槛，完成爱的本质升华。

既然母爱里包含着如此分明和严格的界限，我们有什么理由坚持——母爱就一定是我们接受爱的完善楷模呢？

所以，我宁可说，爱是没有天造地设的老师的，爱又无法无师自通。爱很艰巨，爱要我们在时间中苦苦摸索。

All That Is Motherly Love

Some say we are born with the capacity to love. Maternal love is the best example that helps us appreciate love.

However, I take issue with this notion. I believe love requires learning, consultation, and a lot of practice. Love has to be put to the test and critiqued, with lessons to be learned. You may also need help with it, read up on it, and talk it over, so as to be timely enlightened. In short, love is an art to be honed and perfected through practice.

What comes with birth is but our animal instinct. Love is not something predetermined by your genes, like your eye colour or your height, but what you acquire in life through its many trials. Higher than instinct, human compassion is immense and all-embracing, and transcends the bond of blood and ethnicity and national boundaries, it is boundless, as the edgeless cosmos.

The story of the wolf child in India is a classic example of animal love. It makes me wonder what would happen if a human mother should be left with a wolf cub. It is most unlikely that she'd breastfeed the cub. It goes to show that even though maternal instinct can be indiscriminate, that of humans is not necessarily so. You might argue: Who would be silly enough to feed a wolf cub that may attack you when it's grown up? Yet, even with a mouse, it is still most unlikely that humans would feed it with breast milk.

In this light, maternal love is largely a basic instinct, rather than a higher kind of love. A newborn's experience of maternal love is passive and automatic. To the newborn, that love is first and foremost physical; a requisite for survival. Without which, the tiny infant will perish. Thus, at the early stages of an infant's life, maternal love is a blurry fusion of care and sustenance. It will only become better delineated and more spiritual later. Most mothers do the physical part well, taking good care of their children, having them fed, clad and provided for. Yet, they may not all succeed in moving to the next level; transcending the bond of blood, with greater compassion for humanity.

From time to time, we hear stories of shocking cruelty: a child being beaten to death by his mother for getting poor grades. Was it out of love? The gut reaction of many is that it couldn't be. In their mind, love has to be pure and untainted, and allow no fatal errors. Yet, if the child could be brought back to life and asked if his mother had loved them, I believe their answer, in spite of the physical trauma, would have been positive.

Maternal love, at its most primitive level, can often be blind and self-reflexive, bordering on self-pity. A mother with a deprived childhood will likely think to love her children is to have them fed and clad. If she harbours any unfulfilled dream — being a musician or artist, for example, she'd likely drive her children with utter zest to take music or art lessons, in the name of giving them a head start. Not having any higher qualifications herself, she'd egg her children on, all the way to the postdoctoral apex if necessary, so as to purge her own sense of loss and regret. Examples abound, of mothers imposing their own wishes on their offspring, and tragedies are enacted daily, all in the name of "love".

Such "maternal love" affects the physical and emotional growth of the child as an inviolable, autonomous being. Many a family tragedy and character flaw can be traced back to the "motherly love" that has failed to ascend to a higher level. Such maternal love is primitive; mixed with both desirable and detrimental elements.

At a higher level, maternal love means letting go, bravely and resolutely; out of a profound respect for the individual — that each child is unique and different, to be encouraged and helped to live a life of fulfilment and glory. Such love requires cultivation and learning, even for a mother of fine qualities and potential. We have seen too many who have failed in crossing the threshold and attaining the challenging ascendance; ascendance which can only be achieved through ceaseless learning and self-reflection.

Given all its nuances and limitations, maternal love, without doubt, is not necessarily a perfect model for us to learn and experience love.

Rather, there is no natural, perfect teacher of love. Love has to be learned, by us ourselves, through arduous work over time.

购买经验的金币

我不怕矛盾，也不怕纷乱。

如果只有清一色的说法，那么结论也就非常简单了。世界之所以有趣和千姿百态，就因为它们冲突着、统一着，有各种各样的可能性，因此神出鬼没。

在美国的地铁上，我看到一帮参加夏令营的孩子，他们穿着肥大的T恤衫，上面印着一行字"团结是为了差异"。意思是，我们团结起来，并不是抹杀各自的特性，而正是为了保存彼此的不同。真是一个有特色的口号。

经验这种东西，通常都是在危险的情形下学到的。如果总是在安全中，那么人也只会应对平静。做人太舒服的时候，就没有改变。

话虽这样说，真正事到临头的时候，还是很畏惧。特别是对待自己的孩子，只想让他平安顺遂。

有一则广告，说做父母的总想把世界上最好的东西都给孩子。我能理解这种心情，不过，什么是最好的东西呢？除了推荐名牌奶粉之外，还有面对大千世界的经验。

而经验这种东西，是普通的金钱买不到的。购买经验的金币，就是危难。

For the Acquisition of Experience

I do not shun contradictory views. Nor do I fear discord.

If there were no disagreements, we would be bored to death by easy conclusions. It is the clash and convergence of views, yielding possibilities of every kind, that makes the world an interesting place — a world of tremendous diversity.

Once, while riding the subway in the US, I saw a bevy of summer camp kids, each wearing a loose-fitting T-shirt printed with the slogan "United for Diversity." Apparently, it meant solidarity for the sake of preserving differences and not at the expense of individuality. It was very refreshing.

We acquire useful experience often in situations of danger.

Should we never be exposed to peril, we would be capable only of functioning in a safe environment. We won't accomplish any change if we choose to stay in our comfort zone.

Having said that, I admit I still have fear when facing a moment of truth, especially when it involves my child. I wanted nothing untoward but safe and plain sailing for him.

As one ad tagline proclaims, parents want the best for their children. I can understand the sentiment in statements like that. Yet, what really is "best?" Besides brand name formula milk, the list should include experience they should have for surviving on their own in the real world.

Experience, however, is not something that can be bought with money. The token for its acquisition comes in the form of peril and challenge.

苦难不是牛痘疫苗

那一年几乎成了我的"说话年"。北大、清华、北京师范大学、北京外国语大学、中国协和医科大学、北京科技大学、首都师范大学、中医药大学……还有女子中学和北京八中的少年班。从少年到青年，从北京到新疆，我都曾和他们聊过天。

我之所以不喜欢把那种形式称为讲演，是因为自己心里有障碍。我害怕那个"演"字，觉得有几分虚拟与矫情。也许对在舞台上的演员是正常事情，但对以笔为幕的我来说，更习惯在黎明或是夜半，独自思索。

生平不会表演，也未曾当过老师。面对许多人说话，提前就会感到莫大压力。每逢答应了要在某时某刻与众人会晤，我在前一天就惶惶不可终日，夜里也睡不好觉，仿佛面临一场结果莫测的考试。有时直到赶赴会场的路上，都不晓得自己将如何开头。

其实，这种场合，拒绝是最简单的方法，过去多年我坚持说"不"，除非极熟识的朋友托到头上、百推无效，否则绝不答应出席。一天，女作家赵玫的一句话改变了我的看法。她说，不要拒绝大学生，他们是希望。

这种集体聊天大致分为两部分。前三分之二时间由我主说，题目通常是"文学与人生"这类大得吓人的题目。题目大了，其实有好处，就是无论你怎样说都不会跑题。我私下里以为，同学们对从作家那里能听到些什么，期望值并不很高，一般来说比较宽容，我也乐得撒开来谈。

后三分之一的时间一般留作大家对话。纸条不断从会场的不同角落传上来，形态各异。有写满了字的整张作业纸，也有寥寥数语、窄如柳眉的短笺。我满怀兴致地阅读它们，好像对着大山呼唤了一声，片刻后收获连绵不绝的回音。每次讲演回来，都有成包的各色纸条回馈，纷纷扬扬，好似从飘飘洒洒的冬夜掬回一捧雪花。

我很喜欢这些纸条，里面蕴涵着信息和挑战。时间久了，纸条如山，偶有翻看，仍会感到灼热与激荡。那是一些年轻的心的切片，标记着那些难忘的夜晚。不论日子过去多久，依然显现着清晰的思想和蓬勃的生命力。

我也常常反思，自己在当时的回答中是否诚挚、友善和机智？

现在，我把一些纸条直录在这里。其后是我的回答，基本上是当时的想法，也许经过时间的沉淀更有条理了一些。

问：您不愿当医生，可我最爱看您笔下的医生，这也曾让我一度非常想当医生。您笔下的医生医术都很高超，我觉得您当医生也一定是个好医生，我总为您感到后悔。想问两个问题：

（一）您后悔吗？

（二）您认为作家是最适合您的职业吗？

此条来自清华大学。他们的纸条和别的大学的纸条有些微不同，基本上都用整张的纸，字也写得较大，感觉较为豪放。文科学校所用的纸条多半细小精致，字也文秀些。

答：我当医生的时候，医术一般，但我是一个比较负责任的医生。医生是一个对责任感要求非常严格的职业，甚至可以说，责任感与医术是一个好医生飞翔的双翼。我当医生时有一个习惯，也可以算爱好吧——和病人谈话，耐心倾听他们对于自己痛苦的倾诉。我不喜欢那种医生，把诊断搞清后就不屑于理睬病人，觉得病人只是一个悬挂疾病的衣架。我愿意尽我的所能和气地深入浅出地向病人解释他的病情，同情他的疾苦……这不是很难的事情，但有些医生忽略了。

不当医生，我不后悔。因为这是我在没有外力胁迫的情况下，自觉自愿做出的选择。人一生能够从事自己所热爱的事业是一种奢侈的好运气。

问：您为什么没有起一个笔名？您若起一个笔名，将是什么样的？

此条来自北京大学。直觉告诉我这是一个有志从事文学创作的女孩子。她的提问很内行，富有技术性。

答：在我还没有做好小说能够发表的心理准备的时候，它就发表了，多少有些令我措手不及。当时杂志社并没有人问我要不要用一个笔名，我也就不便说请把原稿上我的本名涂掉，换一个笔名，私下觉得那太给人添麻烦了（其实不复杂，但我不好意思说）。于是，以精心策划的笔名面世的机会稍纵即逝。当然，到了发表第二篇稿子的时候，已从容了些，有机会缓缓思忖一个笔名。但一旦开始具体操作，深深的忧虑攫住了我——换了一个崭新的笔名，我的父母在感情上是否会接受，承认那个铅字所组成的陌生字眼就是他们的女儿？我拿不定主意，也没有勇气问他们。事情一耽搁，机遇就又过去了。我从小是一个很乐意让父母高兴的孩子，为了这份并非空穴来风的忧虑，我终于坚定地不用笔名了。

如果要起笔名，我要用一种矿物质或是金属的名称做笔名。我喜欢那种在亿万斯年的大自然当中凝结精华与力量的感觉，而且我觉得金属有特殊的壮丽。

问：您有那么坎坷的经历，可无论是您的文学和您的话语，所表达的都是对生活的乐观和轻松，您认为这是一种经历了太多苦难后的宽容和超越，还是您并不认为有必要感受沉重？

这个纸条，我记得来自一位医学生，好像还是博士班的。我当时有些踌躇，不知如何解答是好。因为他似乎比我考虑得更成熟。

答：我很坎坷吗？我不觉得啊。现在很多人讲到坎坷的时候，多用一种夸耀的口气或是藏着求人怜悯的企图，使我不爱说这个词。坎坷和顺利似乎是反义词，其实都是生命的相对状态。至于顺利是否就与快乐相连，坎坷是否就一定指向沉重，我以为并非必然。我们可以在顺利的时候愁容惨淡，也可以在苦难时欢颜一笑，关键在于我们把握命运的能力。

我不喜欢模拟苦难，无论是从理论还是从实践上。我对人为地制造苦难以考验他人的做法深恶痛绝。人生的苦难，不是像牛痘疫苗一样的病毒提取物，植入人体就可以终生预防天花了。我所看到的更多的事实是，苦难磨秃了人对美好事物的细腻感受力，催生了损人利己的恶性竞争意识，使人变得粗糙和狠毒。苦难浪费了时间，剥夺了本应更富创造力的年华，迟滞了我们的步伐。

如果苦难一定要扑面而来，那就得镇静迎战了。这另当别论。

我所遇到的最好玩的一些问题，比如关于未来和幻想，事无巨细的提问和随心所欲的对话来自少年，特别是北京八中。那是一些十三四岁的男孩女孩，智商很高，天性活泼生动，马上就要参加高考了，竟然还有兴致邀我对话，说读过我的作品，想交流一下感受。

我力拒，理由简单。我想象不出这些非凡的孩子会是怎样的精灵，不知和太聪明的孩子该如何讲话。万一不妥，岂不是戕害了祖国花朵，还是一些很优良的大花骨朵。闹不好，我前脚刚走，后脚人家就得消毒。

但校方力邀，那位音色有些苍凉的老师，一口一个，不是我请您，是我的孩子请您。

做母亲的人听不得人家说我的孩子想如何如何，我只好答应了。

所幸那是一群非常机灵可爱的少年，知识面极广，天上地下、金戈铁马，我们讨论了很多问题，留下深刻记忆的是这样一张纸条。

问：我考上大学一点儿问题都没有，但我不喜欢这件事，今年七月我不想考啦！背许多没用的东西，瞎耽误工夫。顺便问您一句，您第一次稿费钱多吗？干什么用了？

答：人一生要干许多自己不喜欢的事。这一规则以我的岁数和经历来看，可以倚老卖老地向你们说——这是一条铁律。世上有些事不是因为我们喜欢才去做，而是从长远看、从责任看、从发展的眼光看必须做。我同意你的观点，上大学没什么了不起，但它是一张门票，你要领略更广大的景色，你得有入场券。不必将它看得过重，也不可太掉以轻心。你既然一点儿问题都没有，不妨轻松过关，然后再按自己的意志努力向前，走自己的路。

　　第一次稿费钱不多，几万字的稿子，几百块钱，基本上合一个字一分多点钱。我把其中一半寄给我父母，另一半买了书。妈妈说，汇款单到的那一天，她正在小路上散步，听人喊"你女儿把稿费寄来了"，几乎流下了眼泪。

No Vaccine for Suffering

I did so many talks that year that I called it my "Prodigal Year of Talks." I travelled from Beijing to Xinjiang, talking with high school and college students. I found myself speaking at Peking University, Tsinghua University, Beijing Normal University, Beijing Foreign Studies University, Peking Union Medical College, Beijing University of Science and Technology, Capital Normal University, University of Traditional Chinese Medicine, as well as the Girls' High School of Beijing and the LEAP program at the Beijing No. 8 High School.

I didn't like them to be called speeches, for I was averse to contrivance in the act of speech-giving. What comes effortlessly to the stage actor is never my thing. I am more accustomed to musing in the solitude of the wee hours and dawn, with the blank page being my stage.

Thus, I am no actor. Nor have I ever been a teacher or instructor. I always felt edgy before speaking in front of a group. I'd be on pins and needles all day and my sleep would be fitful the night before a meeting with a large group of people, as if it were some tough exam. Sometimes, I'd be still at a loss as to how I should start when I was already on my way to the venue.

In truth, the simplest would be to decline any invitation to speak. For years, I had done just that, except when it was a request by very close friends which I couldn't turn down. Then, one day the woman writer Zhao Mei changed my mind with her advice, "Never turn away college students for they are the hope of the future."

Such talks were usually set up with two segments. I would talk for about two thirds of the time, with such grand sounding topics as "Literature and Life." One advantage with such topics is: you could ramble on without risking being too far off the mark. I assumed students wouldn't expect too much from a writer's talk. Since they would be relaxed, I was more than happy to talk about such broad topics.

The remainder of these sessions were for dialogue. Questions written on strips of paper were passed on to me. They'd be conveyed from all corners of the room in any odd shape or form — a page with a few scribbled lines, torn off from an exercise book, or a tiny scrap of paper with just a few words. They enthralled me in my post-talk glow, as if echoes bouncing back to me after I bellowed atop a hill. I would head home with a bundle of these rainbow-coloured paper slips, cherishing them as if they were the exquisite snowflakes in the first snow of winter.

I enjoyed reading them — provocative in thinking and never short on substance. Over time, a mountain of them piled up. I'd leaf through them occasionally and be touched still by the youthful energy and vigour in them. Refreshing, inspiring and full of verve, the messages they carry always put me in mind of those memorable evenings long ago.

Looking back, I often wondered if I had been sincere, gracious and witty enough with my answers at the time.

Here I list some of the questions as they were posed, and my answers to them, largely reflecting my thinking then, with some tweaking later for clarity.

— Q: You said you didn't aspire to be a doctor. Yet, your stories about doctors with great medical skills were my favourite, and they once inspired me to ponder a medical career. I think you would have made a very good doctor. I felt sorry for your not doing so. My questions:

1) Don't you have any regret?

2) Do you think you were cut out for being a writer?

This was from a student of Tsinghua University. Their slips of paper were slightly different than those I got at other colleges. Questions were always written on full pages, and in large, vigorous script. In contrast, questions from the liberal arts colleges were often written in a delicate hand and on tiny strips of fine paper.

— A: When I worked as a medical doctor, I had a rather strong sense of responsibility but average skills. The former is mandatory for the medical profession. Both responsibility and skills are requisites for being a good doctor. I made it a point to always talk with my patients, something I also enjoyed doing — lending a sympathetic ear to their suffering. I detest those who, once they have established a diagnosis, wouldn't bother to talk with their patients any more, treating them as mere walking examples of medical conditions. I tried, to the extent possible, to explain to my patients their conditions in a way that is easier for them to understand, with a warm and supportive attitude. This is not difficult to do. Yet some doctors have neglected doing it.

I don't regret leaving the medical profession. It was a choice I made without any external pressure. I count myself as being very lucky and privileged to do what I love as a career.

— Q: Why don't you have a penname? What would it be, if you were to use one?

This was from a student at Peking University. I had a hunch that this was a girl who aspired to be a writer. Her line of questioning was shrewd, almost expert-like.

— A: I was caught somewhat by surprise when my first story got published. I wasn't prepared for it. No one at the magazine asked me if I wanted to use a penname. I felt awkward to ask them to replace my name on the manuscript with a penname, fearing it might be too bothersome (It wouldn't be; I was just too shy to ask.) So I let the chance of having a well-thought-out penname for my literary debut slip by. I was more relaxed by the time my second story was published. I could think up a penname at my leisure. However I was seized with anxiety once I started going about it. What would my parents think — seeing the strange name in print that was supposed to be their daughter's? I hesitated and shied away from asking them about it. It was put on hold and the opportunity slipped through my fingers. I had been eager to please my parents since I was little. To save myself any agony, I decided not to bother.

If I were to choose a penname, I would opt for the name of a mineral or metal. I am always amazed by the power of geological transformation over eons of time that have produced minerals. And I think metals have a special kind of beauty.

— Q: There is so much optimism and light-heartedness in your writings and talks, even though you've been through a lot of hardships in life. Does this reflect a generosity of spirit transcending suffering, or a preference for not dwelling on the dreadful weight of being?

I remember this came from a medical student, probably already on a doctoral program. I hesitated and wasn't sure how to respond. He seemed to have already given it more thought than

I did.

— A: Did I have more than my fair share of hardships in life? I don't think so. Many now talk about hardship as if it were something to brag about, or with the dubious intent to inspire pity. Because of this, I try not to use such a word. Adversity seems to be the antithesis of prosperity. Yet they are both transient states of human existence. I do not agree it's a given that prosperity leads to happiness and adversity suffering. We can be terribly glum in moments of comfort and success, but laugh in the face of suffering. It all depends on our inner strength and capacity to take destiny in our own hands.

— I deplore, with utter disgust, the notion and practice of putting people to the test, just to see how they could endure suffering. Suffering is not something that you could be fortified against through deliberate exposure, like getting a vaccine shot for smallpox; once done, you are immune for life. If anything, suffering, more often than not, blunts our nuanced sense of beauty and gives rise to vicious, everyman-for-himself competition, bringing out the worst and ugliest in people.

Suffering held up progress and lives that could have been more productive were wasted.

— Yet if suffering befalls us, we will just have to face it with calm. But that's another topic altogether.

Some of the most interesting questions came from younger audiences, such as students from Beijing No. 8 High School. They were boys and girls in their early teens; smart, energetic and lively; unrelenting and whimsical in their questioning which spanned topics from imagination to visions of future. I was amazed that, with the National College Entrance Examination not far down the road, they were still keen to have a dialogue with me. They wanted to share their thoughts with me after reading my stories, so they said.

I had tried to decline. I simply couldn't imagine how elfish these smart kids were. I didn't know how I should talk with them. I couldn't risk impressing these young people — "Flowers of our Motherland," and very fine ones at that — with remarks that could be deemed wide of the mark. I did not want to end up making them feel compelled to "detoxify" on the heels of my visit.

However, the school's representative was persistent, pleading almost in a tone of despair, "Please accept this invitation from my children — the young pupils."

Being a mother myself, I couldn't snub someone conveying a wish of children. I had to oblige.

Luckily, they were a lovely group of smart young students, with a remarkable breadth of knowledge. We talked freely about a wide range of topics and I could sense their imaginations soared. What impressed me most was the following question.

— Q: I won't have any trouble getting into college. But I don't like the way it is done. I am not going to sit for the national examination this coming July. Having to memorize so much that is useless is simply a waste of time. By the way, how much were you paid for your first story? What did you spend it on?

— A: In life, oftentimes we must act out of necessity rather than preference. Having become wiser with age, I must say this holds true for everyone. An iron law! There are things we must do for the sake of the long-term, our responsibility and our potential. I agree with you — getting into college is no big deal. Yet it is a ticket to a future of richer experience. We need neither exaggerate nor belittle its importance. Since you don't see it as insurmountable, why not take it in stride? You can always endeavour to follow the path that suits your fancy later.

— I wasn't paid much for my first story. A few hundred yuan paid for a story of less than a hundred thousand words. It came to a little over one cent per word. I sent half of what I was paid to my parents. The rest I spent on books. My mother told me she was out for a walk when the postman delivered the money order. When she heard someone calling out "Your daughter has sent you her royalties for her story!" she was almost in tears.

购买一个希望

那年在国外，看到一个穷苦老人在购买彩票。他走到彩票售卖点，还没来得及说话，工作人员就手脚麻利地在电脑上为他选出了一组数字，然后把凭证交给他。他好像无家可归，没有什么固定的目标要赶赴，买完彩票，就在一旁呆呆站着。我正好空闲，便和他聊起来。

我问，你为什么不亲自选一组数字呢？

他说，是我自己选的。我总在这里买彩票。工作人员知道我要哪一组数字。只要看到我走近，就会为我敲出来。

我说，那你每次选的数字都是一样的喽？

他说，是的。是一样的。我已经以同样的数字买了整整四十年彩票。每周一次，购买一个希望。

我心中快速计算着，一年就算五十二周，四五二十，二五一十……然后再乘以每注彩票的花费……天！我问道，你中过吗？

他突然变得忸怩起来，喃喃说，没中过。有一次，大奖和我选的数字只差一个。

我说，那以后，你还选这组数字吗？

他很坚定地说，选。

我说，我是个外行，说错了你别见怪。依我猜，以后重新出现这组数字的概率是极低的，更别说还得有一个数字改成符合你的要求。

他说，你说得对，是这样的。

我就愣了。他衣衫褴褛面容憔悴。买彩票的钱虽然不多，但周复一周地买着，粒米成箩，也积成了不算太小的数目。用这些钱，为什么不给自己买一身蔽寒的衣服，吃一顿饱饭呢？再说，固执地重复同一组数字，绝不更改，实在也非明智之举。

我不忍伤他心，又不知说什么好，只有久久地沉默了。过了一会儿，他主动开口说，你一定很想知道那是一组什么样的数字吧？

我点头说，是啊。

他有些害羞地说，那是我初恋女友的生辰数字。每周我下注的时候，都会想起她，心中就暖和起来。

我说，那到了开奖的时候，你知道自己没中，会不会心中寒冷？

他笑了，牙齿在霓虹灯下像糖衣药片一样变换着色彩。他说，不会。我马上又买新的一轮彩票，希望就又长出来了。我很穷，属于穷人的希望是很有限的。用这么少的钱，就能买到一个礼拜的快乐，这种机会，在这个世界上，实在是不多。更不用说，那个数字还寄托着我的回忆。如果我选的这组数字中大奖，她一定会注意到的，因为那是她的生辰啊。紧接着她会好奇是谁得了这份奖金？于是就能看到我的名字。她立刻就会明白我这一辈子没有忘记她，而且我有了这么多的钱，她也许会来找我……

老人说完，就转过身，缓缓地走了。

后来，我把这个真实的故事讲给很多人听。每个人听完后都会长久地沉默。然后说，真盼望他中奖啊！

Buying a Ticket of Hope

Years ago on an overseas trip, I saw a poor old man at a lottery kiosk. As it was his turn, the clerk behind the counter quickly punched a few keys and produced a ticket with the numbers selected, before the old man even uttered a word. Standing with a blank stare after getting his lottery ticket and probably homeless, he was apparently not in a hurry to go anywhere specific. Similarly disposed at that moment, I struck up a conversation.

—Why didn't you pick your own numbers? I asked the old man.

—Those were my numbers, he said. I always buy my lotto

tickets here. They know what numbers I want and will have my ticket printed when they see me coming.

— So, always the same numbers? I asked.

— Right. The same numbers for the last forty years. One ticket every week. Buying a ticket for hope, if you like.

I did some quick mental calculation. Once a week and, minus a few odd weeks for holidays, at least 52 weeks each year; to be multiplied by the cost of each ticket....

— Good heavens! Did you ever win?

— Not yet, he turned coy suddenly, muttering. Once I had a close miss for winning the jackpot; with just one digit off.

— You kept using the same numbers after that? I asked.

— Sure, he said without hesitation.

— I know little about lottery, I said. So forgive me if I am wrong. It seems highly unlikely the same winning numbers would ever come up again — not to mention your numbers were off any way.

— You were right, he admitted. So it is.

I was dumbfounded. He looked pale and haggard, in his threadbare clothes. Although it doesn't cost much to get a lottery ticket now and then, they do add up if you buy it week after week. He could have used the money to buy himself a good meal from time to time or clothes to keep him warm. Besides, it doesn't seem wise to keep playing the same numbers. Yet, I didn't have the heart to say so, for fear of hurting him. At a loss for words, I fell silent. After a while, he broke the silence, "You must be keen on knowing what those numbers are, aren't you?"

— You bet! I nodded.

— They are the birthday numbers of my first girlfriend, he said shyly. The thought of her warms my heart every week when I plays the lottery.

— Did it chill you when the winning numbers were announced and you didn't win? I asked.

He broke into a smile, his teeth, in the blinking neon light, taking on colours like assorted pills.

—No, he said. It won't be long before I am hopeful and play again. I am a man of little means and hope is a luxury. With just a little money, you can get a whole week of joyful hope. A bargain you don't get anywhere else. Besides, my lottery numbers bring back sweet memories. If I ever win, the winning numbers that match her birthday would surely catch her attention. She will wonder who the winner is and find my name. She will realize instantly I haven't forgotten her all this time. She might even come back to me with the windfall landing in my lap...

With that, the old man turned and slowly walked away.

I recounted this true story to many who, after falling silent for a long moment, invariably prayed, "If only he could win!"

爱的回音壁

现今中年以下的夫妻，几乎都是只有一个孩子，关爱之心，大概达到了中国有史以来的最高值。家的感情就像个苹果，姐妹兄弟多了，就会分成好几瓣儿。若是千亩一苗，孩子在父母的乾坤里便独步天下了。

在前所未有的爱意中浸泡的孩子，是否感到莫大的幸福？我好奇地问过。孩子们撇嘴说，不，没觉着谁爱我们。

我震住了。一个不懂得爱的孩子，就像不会呼吸的鱼，出了家庭的水箱，在干燥的社会上，他不爱人，也不自爱，必将焦渴而死。

可是，你怎样让由你一手哺育长大的孩子懂得什么是爱呢？从他的眼睛接受第一缕光线时，已被无微不至的呵护包围，早已对关照体贴熟视无睹。生物学上有一条规律，当某种物质过于浓烈时，感觉迅速迟钝、麻痹……

寒霜陡降也能使人感悟幸福，比如父母离异或是早逝。但它是灾变的副产品，带着天力人力难违的僵冷。孩子虽然在追忆中明白了什么是被爱，那却是一间正常人家不愿走进的教室。

孩子降生人间，原应一手承接爱的乳汁，一手播撒爱的甘霖，爱是一本收支平衡的账簿。可惜从一开始，成人就间不容发地倾注了所有爱的储备，劈头盖脑砸下，把孩子的一只手塞得太满。全是收入，没有支出，爱沉淀着、淤积着，从神奇化为腐朽，反而让孩子无法感到别人是爱他的。

我又问一群孩子，那你们什么时候感到别人是爱你的呢？

没指望得到像样的回答。一个成人都争执不休的问题，孩子能懂多少？没想到，孩子的答案明朗、坚定。

我爸下班回来，我给他倒了一杯水，因为我刚在幼儿园里学了一首歌，词里说的是给妈妈倒水，可是我妈还没回来呢，我就先给爸爸倒了。我爸只说了一句，好儿子……就流泪了。从那次起，我知道他是爱我的。光头小男孩说。

我给奶奶耳朵上插了一朵花，要是别人，她才不让呢，马上就得揪下来。可那是我插的，她一直戴着，见着人就说，看，这是我孙女打扮我呢……我知道她最爱我了……另一个女孩说。

　　我大大地惊异了，讶然这些事的碎小和孩子们铁的逻辑，更感动于他们谈论里的郑重神气和结论的斩钉截铁。爱与被爱高度简化了、统一了。孩子在被他人需要时，感到了一个幼小生命的意义。成人注视并强调了这种价值，他们就感悟到深深的爱意，在尝试给予的同时，他们懂得了什么是接受。爱是一面辽阔光滑的回音壁，微小的爱意反复回响着、折射着，变成巨大的轰鸣。当付出的爱被隆重地接受并珍藏时，孩子终于强烈地感觉到被爱的尊贵与神圣。

　　天下的父母，如果你爱孩子，一定让他从力所能及的时候开始爱你和周围的人。这绝非成人的自私，而是为孩子的一世着想的远见。不要抱怨孩子天生无爱，爱与被爱是铁杵成针、百年树人的本领，就像走路一样，需要反复练习，才会健步如飞。

　　如果把孩子在无边无际的爱里泡得口眼翻白，

早早剥夺了他感知爱的能力，育出一个爱的低能儿，即使不算弥天大错，也是成人权力的滥施，或许要遭天谴。

　　在爱中领略被爱，会有加倍的丰收。孩子渐渐长大，一个爱自己、爱世界、爱人类也爱自然的青年，便喷薄欲出了。

Love's Echo Shall Ring

Single-child family has long been the norm in Chinese society — starting with the baby-boomers who became parents. The kind of adult attention heaped on children in single-child families is without equal in Chinese history. The only children are the centre of their parents' universe, monopolizing their affection, unlike kids with siblings in earlier generations who must compete for such affection.

Yet, do children growing up with such unprecedented affection appreciate the love they received? I once asked several kids out of curiosity. Their unanimous answer was "No." Pouting their lips, they said they didn't feel particularly loved ...

I was dumbfounded. A child growing up not knowing how to appreciate love will not thrive when he strikes out on his own, for he will not have the capacity to love himself and others. He will be fragile and doomed to fail, once outside his sheltered home, like fish out of water.

How, then, do you teach love to the child you are bringing up by hand? He has been pampered with, and grown used to, all the affection since the first ray of sunshine caught his eye. As in physiology, when a stimulus is too strong and persistent, it soon reaches saturation — making its recipient numb and oblivious...

A sudden reversal of fortune can have the effect of making us more appreciative of what we once had. A child may come to understand love, albeit retrospectively, after a significant life event, such as his parents' divorce or the loss of a parent, which in itself may give him a sense of helplessness and inevitability. Such heightened understanding and appreciation is the "by-product" of a calamitous experience; yet out of bounds for the usual, happy family.

Every child born into this world should be nurtured with love and give love in return. Love is about giving and accepting; a balanced book. However, the only children are showered with all the affection from the very start of their lives. Love to them is all about taking and no giving. Love fills their little world to the hilt and soon loses its magic, turning from the sublime to prosaic. At the end of the day, they cannot even feel others' love any more.

Again, I asked a bevy of children to think of instances when they felt loved by others, not expecting much in the way of decent answers, for such a question probably would leave even adults quarrel no end. To my surprise, their answers were clear and certain:

— For me it was after I poured a glass of water for Dad when he came home from work. I had just learned from a nursery rhyme that says something about pouring a glass of water for Mom. Mom was not home yet. So I did it for Dad. All he said was "Good boy" and his eyes were moist with tears. I knew then that he loves me, so said the little boy with a shaved head.

— I put a flower behind Nana's ear. She wouldn't have let anyone else do that and would have yanked it off if they did. But she wore the flower and told everybody, "Look, my granddaughter decked me out!" I know she loves me most, so said a little girl.

I was amazed by how mundane these events looked and touched by how unequivocal the children were in their logic and conclusion, and their apparent air of seriousness when talking. To love and be loved at the same time, with such beautiful simplicity! In giving love, these kids sensed the significance of their being; feeling intensely loved as their little acts of kindness were emphatically valued and appreciated by adults. In learning to give, they also learned to accept. A humble expression of love, resonating with power and beauty, found an echo in another's heart; the mountain shall answer and the love's echo ring. When a child's gift of love is requited and cherished, he learns how sacred and precious it is to be loved.

To all parents I appeal: if you love your child, you must let him love you and those around him as early as he can. This is for his own good and the life that lies ahead of him, rather than to amuse adults. Do not agonize over your child not knowing how to love. To love and be loved is a lifelong learning enterprise; a skill, like that of an endurance trekker, only to be perfected through persistent practice.

If you shower your child with boundless affection to the point of satiation, desensitizing him to love early on, you will bring up a child incapable of love. It will be a terrible miscarriage of parental duty, though not necessarily a colossal sin, and be harshly judged when the time comes.

Having your child learn to appreciate love

by giving love, you will be doubly rewarded. A child thus growing up will have enough self-love and love for nature, humanity and the world — a fine young person coming of age; a joy to behold.

你永不要说

十年前，我在西部边陲的某部队留守处当军医，主要给随军家属看病。婆姨们的男人都在昆仑山上戍边，家里母子平安，前方的将士就英勇。我的工作很重要。

家眷都是从天南地北会聚来的。原来在农村，地广人稀，空气新鲜，不易患病。现在像羊群似的赶在一起，加之西北干燥寒冷，病人不断，忙得我不亦乐乎。

我的助手是卫生员小鲁，一个四川籍的小个子兵，长得没什么特色，只是一对眼睛又黑又亮，叽里咕噜地转，像蜜炼的中药丸。他没接受过正规培训，连劳动带扔手榴弹加在一起，算上了几个月的卫生员训练班。不过心灵手巧，打针、换药、针灸都在行。每天围着我问这问那，总说学好了本领，回家给他奶奶瞧病去。他奶奶有很严重的气管炎，喘得像堵了一半的烟筒。

一天他对我说，毕医生，我想买点青霉素给我奶奶治病。我给他开了处方，他买了药寄回去。过了些日子，他说奶奶的病比以前好多了，我们都为他高兴。可是青霉素用完了，想再买些。我又给他开了处方，这次他没拿到药。领导说药不多了，工作人员不能老自己买，得留给病人用。

边防站乔站长的独生子小旗病了。我开了青霉素打针，那剂量对一个五岁的孩子来说，足够大的。我向来崇尚毛主席老人家说的集中优势兵力打歼灭战的计策，用地毯式轰炸。

连续打了四天针，孩子的病势丝毫不见轻。我很纳闷，这种怪症最近不断出现，用药像泼凉水一样。好像是一种极耐药的病菌侵袭了孩子。

有人说，这医生的医术不高。这么年轻，自己没生过孩子，哪里会给孩子瞧病？

我说，我还没上过战场呢，可我治好过枪伤。

人们不再说什么，但孩子的病日渐沉重。我只有查书，把厚厚的书页翻得如同柳絮飞花，怕自己贻误了小小的生命。

终于有一天，小旗的妈妈怯生生地问我，您给我儿开的药，是一瓶还是半瓶？

我说，是一瓶啊。

她有些迟疑地说，那小鲁给我家小旗每次打的都是半瓶。

我的心嗖地紧缩成一团，像腊月天里一个冻硬了的馒头。这个小鲁！一定是他克扣了病人的药品，把青霉素私存起来，预备寄回家。

小鲁呀小鲁，这不是儿戏，人命关天！

我该怎么办？

当下顶要紧的是赶快给小旗补上一针。

之后我想了许久。

报告领导吗，小鲁从此就毁了。贪污病人的药品，就是贪污病人的生命。置之不理，更不行。要是让病人家属知道了，要是病人因此有个三长两短，非得有人找他拼命。

我把小鲁叫出来，对他说，小旗的病若是治不好，会转成肾炎、关节炎、心脏病……

他惊愕地瞪圆眼睛，说，真有这么严重？没有人给我们讲过这些，训练班里就讲过打针的时候要慢慢推药，病人不疼。我说，我知道你惦记你的奶奶，可你知道每一个病人都有亲人。你的心里除了装着你的奶奶，也要给别人留个地方……

　　我说，你不要以为打针不过是把一些水推到肉里，就像盐进了大海，谁也看不见。不是的，科学是谁也蒙骗不了的，用了什么药该出现什么疗效，那是一定的。假如出了意外，那可就是出了医院进法院……

　　他的脸变得像包中药丸的蜡壳一样白。

　　他说，毕医生，我……我……

　　我赶快堵住他的嘴，就像黄继光堵枪眼一样果断。哦，别说。什么也别说。世界上有些事情，记住，永不要说。

　　你不说，就没有任何人知道。

　　你不知道我不知道，我们永远都不需要知道。不要把错误想得那么分明。不要去讨论那个过程，把它像标本一样在记忆中固定。有些事情不值得总结，忘记它的最好方法就是绝不回头。也许那事情很严重，但最大的改正是永不重复。

　　小鲁的眼泪流下来。我不怕眼泪，我怕他说话。还好，他很聪明，听懂了我的话，什么也没有说。

　　我长长地吁了一口气。

后来，小旗的病很快好了，留守处再也没有出现过用药不灵的怪症。

再后来，小鲁因为工作认真负责，对病人春风般温暖，被送到军医大学学习，成了一名很优秀的医生。

只是不知他奶奶的病好了没有。有这么孝顺的孙子，该是好了的。

The Best Remedy

Twenty years ago, I was an army doctor at a support base in the western border region. My charge was to care for the military families. If they were taken good care of, the men deployed to the posts high in the Kunlun Mountains would bravely discharge their duty of guarding the border, without anxious thoughts for home. My work was thus very important.

The families at the base were from all over the country, accustomed to life in airy, scattered rural villages. Being squeezed into the family quarters at the base, like skittish sheep brought into an enclosure, which was made worse by the cold climes of the far northwest, rendered many disease prone.

My assistant was Xiao Lu, a young medic. He was from Sichuan Province. Short in stature, he had no distinct features other than two keen black eyes that dart like a sorcerer's. As a medic, he had been given no more than a few months' training, and that included many days for the usual boot camp drills such as throwing dummy hand grenades and physical work. But he was smart, with deft hands, and soon became adept at giving shots, changing dressing and even acupuncture. He shadowed me every day and always had a question or two. He was keen to learn all the medical skills, so that after mustering out he could return to his home village to help take care of his granny. She suffered from severe bronchitis which made her wheeze constantly; like an old chimney begrimed with soot.

One day, he told me he wanted to buy some penicillin for his granny. I gave him a prescription, with which he bought a few dosages and sent them home through the mail. Sometime later, he told me his granny was getting better; but she needed more penicillin shots. I gave him another prescription. Yet he couldn't have it filled this time round, as the administrator had given instructions on priority for patients. He didn't want penicillin being all bought up by the staff, given the low inventory.

Then Xiaoqi, the only son of the border station commander Qiao, fell ill. I prescribed penicillin shots, enough does for a five-year-old. I had always admired Chairman Mao's oft-tried strategy of deploying the best forces for maximum attrition and I wouldn't shy away from using "saturation bombing", so to speak, against germs.

After a wholesome regimen of penicillin injections for four days, the boy showed no sign of improvement. I was rather perplexed. His was not the only case of late. Like water off a duck's back, doses of antibiotics had no effect at all on the nasty germs. It seemed that the boy could have been infected with a very drug-resistant strain of bugs.

—The young doctor is plain incompetent, some began to

doubt. She has never had a child. What does she know about treating sick kids?

— I have not seen battle, yet I have treated battle wounds alright, I retorted.

This did shut them up. However, the boy was not getting any better. I turned to medical books. Thumbing through the hefty volumes, and their pages flashing before my eyes in a blurred animation, I began to worry that the boy's life might slip away on my watch.

At last, the boy's mother asked me timidly, "The shots you prescribed for my son — are they supposed to be in full vials?"

— Yes, I confirmed.

— Then why did Mr. Lu always use half-filled vials on my son? she asked hesitantly.

My heart sank. So Xiao Lu was short changing the patients. He must have put aside some of the penicillin shots and sent them home. How could he do that? He had put patient's life at stake! This was no trivial matter! What should I do? First things first. I gave the boy a booster shot right away.

With that done, I pondered on the matter long and hard. If I reported this to my superiors, Xiao Lu's army career would be done for. To short change patients was tantamount to stealing their chances for recovery and healing. If I turned a blind eye to this, he'd carry on with what he did. There would be hell to pay, should something untoward happen to the patient and patient's family find out sooner or later.

So I pulled Xiao Lu aside and said sternly, "Should Xiaoqi's conditions not improve, he may develop complications such as nephritis, arthritis or heart infection ... "

— It's that serious? he was shocked, eyes nearly popping out of his head. Nobody told me so. All I was told in training was to push the plunger slowly to avoid causing pain.

— I know you care about your grandma, I said. You should know that every patient may have someone who cares about them, too. So you should have their interests at heart, in addition to your granny's…. Giving injections is not just an act of pushing liquid into the muscle and whatever goes in simply disappears, like salt dissolving water, leaving trace. No one can cheat science — a medication will produce a certain effect. If something should go wrong, someone might very well end up in court….

His face turned ashen, like the waxy shell of a large herbal pill.

— Doctor Bi, I…, he muttered.

— Say no more! I cut him short right there, like plugging the leaky hole up with a cork. Remember, there are things you should remain silent about. No one will ever know if you don't tell. Neither you nor I. No one needs to ever know. Don't fear that your mistake may be all too glaring. No more discussion of how it was made. Don't commit it memory, like a mounted specimen in a glass case. Sometimes it's best not to look back. The error may be grave, yet the best remedy is simply never repeating it.

By then, Xiao Lu was in tears. I dreaded his further babbling. Luckily, he had his own wit and saw my point. He spoke no more and I heaved a sigh of relief.

Xiaoqi soon recovered. There were also no more cases of drug-resistant infections at the base.

Still later, Xiao Lu was offered an opportunity to study at an Army Medical School, in recognition of his strong work ethics and dedicated service. He eventually became a fine medical doctor.

I have heard nothing further about his long-suffering granny. I like to think that with such a caring grandchild, she must have long since healed.

生病也是生活

《自助看医生》这篇小文，讲的是我和儿子的一个生活片段，几乎完全是原始风貌，我不过是按照时间的顺序直接记录下来。多年来，我在创作中基本遵循着一个原则：小说可以虚构，但散文几乎都是真事。二者在我这里的区别，大致相当于艺术摄影和纪实的老照片。我们之所以今天还对那些遥远年代的泛着橙黄色的卷边照片，双眸聚焦心存暖意——因为它们曾经的真实。

这篇小文选给五年级的孩子们看，真是十分合适。事情发生的年代，我儿子正巧也是这个年龄段，同学们读起来，也许会有几分亲切感。这些年来，我碰到过若干位家长，跟我说他们喜欢这篇文章，有几位干脆说他们曾模仿这篇文章描写的步骤，让病中的孩子独自去看病。

人是会病的，孩子也不能幸免。生病是生活的一部分，父母不能包办一切。我一直秉承这一思路，来处理自己和孩子的关系。

父母爱孩子，是天性和本能。如何教育孩子，需要学习和实践，本能管不了那么多。孩子一天天长大，能做的事情、能思考的问题逐日增加，越来越多。一切都是在潜移默化中发生，并没有什么人正儿八经地向我们宣告骤变从哪一个时刻开始。爸爸妈妈这个职务，是世界上最难胜任的角色之一，充满了艺术性和不确定性。

我是医生出身，始终觉得生病不要大惊小怪，不过是生活的颤音，只有按部就班欣然接受，从容面对。看过一个纪录片，说的是狮子如何教后代捕获猎物，妈妈非常认真和周到，甚至不惜向小狮子发脾气，撕咬它们，以求让孩子们习得正确的捕猎方法……我很感动，心想一个动物尚且如此言传身教，作为人类的母亲，爱孩子，要有目的有步骤地训练孩子奔跑和翱翔的能力。

有一位女性告诉我，儿子上大学在武汉，某天早上起来不舒服，请了假躺在床上。到了中午，觉得身上发冷，可能是发烧了。同学们到校外参观，也没人回来。男生很害怕，就给他远在北京的妈妈打电话，说，我快要死了，你救救我。妈妈说，你赶快到医院去看病啊。他说，我不会看病。妈妈百般无奈之下，给当地一个朋友打电话，求他放下自己的工作，到××大学宿舍楼，带自己的孩子去看病。那个朋友就打了车，跨过长江到了大学区，好容易才找到男孩，把他送到医院，最后诊断是重感冒。这位妈妈对我说，我要是早点看到你的这篇文章就好了，也不必让人家跨过长江去救我的孩子。

我的这篇小文是从一个妈妈的眼光和心情来写的，不知道孩子们能不能体会到母亲的百感交集——那种既想让孩子锻炼成长，又怕孩子遭受磨难的复杂心理。结尾部分"聊胜于无"一句，可能稍微有点绕。我的本意是：无论一个妈妈对自己的孩子倾注了多少心血，每个人的路还是要自己走。当长辈的只能为孩子们提供一张大致的路线图，可能和现实生活还有很大的距离。归根结底，路是要自己走的。

我有一个小小的建议。给同学们布置一个作业：到医院去一趟，搞清楚看病的程序。或者描写一件发生在医院的事情。这对拓展孩子们的视野，也许有帮助。

To Be Ill Is Human

A Do-It-Your Visit to the Doctor is a true story revolving around my son and me; a slice of life, realistically documented in a chronological order. Over the years, I have largely followed the rule that while novels are fictional, essays should be mostly about real-life experiences. The difference for me is akin to that between art photography and candid old photos. We are riveted by photos from the distant past, with their frayed corners and yellowish tint, because they strike a chord, with their raw realism and being utterly true to a life that once was.

The essay was selected for a reading list for fifth graders; a fitting choice, for the story took place when my son was about that age. They will find it somewhat true to their life. I have met quite a few parents over the years who told me they liked the story. Some even followed the steps recounted in the essay to have their kids do a do-it-your visit to the doctor!

People get sick, and children are no exception. Such is life. Parents can't always do everything for their children. This has been my thinking in handling the relationship with my child.

Parental love is a natural instinct. However, it takes more than instinct to properly bring up a child, which requires learning and practice. As children grow up, their abilities to think and act increase by the day. Yet, at first, change can be subtle and barely noticeable. There is not going to be a precise point in time when the transformation is declared to momentarily start. The role of parenting is one of the most challenging in life. With so many uncertainties involved, it is very much a form of art.

Having been trained to be a doctor, I have always advised calm and not to panic over illness. Getting sick is but a glitch in everyday life. We will just have to accept and have it dealt with when it comes. I once saw a documentary about how lions teach cubs to hunt. A lioness took the business of training very seriously. She roared and charged, so that the cubs could learn to hunt the right way. Lions teaching their young by example...
It touched a chord. As humans, we should also, purposefully and methodically, train our young to run and soar in their own right.

A woman once told me the story about her son, a college student in Wuhan. After waking up one morning feeling under the weather, he called in sick and went back to bed. By noon, he had started having the chills, likely running a fever. As his roommates had left for an outing, nobody checked in on him. He began to panic and called his mother in Beijing, "I think I am going to die, Mom. Help me!" His mother said, "Go and see a doctor right now." However, he said he didn't know how. His mother, in a pinch, called a friend of hers in that town and begged him to drop everything, go to the dorm and take his son to a doctor. The man had to take a taxi to get to the college district on the other side of the Yangtze River. He only managed to find the boy after considerable trouble. The boy was diagnosed as having a bad cold at the hospital. His mother said, "Should I have read your story earlier, I could have saved my friend a bothersome trip across the Yangtze!"

I wrote that story from the perspective, and with the feeling, of a mother. I wasn't quite sure then if young readers could see the dilemma that mothers have — wanting their children to learn to be strong on one hand; worrying about what they might be put through on the other. I concluded my story by saying that my approach may be of very little worth, if any, to others. What I meant was that children learn what they live, no matter how much love, attention, and words of wisdom are given by their mothers. What parents can give is at most a rough roadmap, which may be quite different from what's in the real world. In the end, everyone has to find his or her own path.

To conclude, I have a little suggestion to my young readers: take on an assignment of visiting a hospital and learning the exact procedures of consulting a doctor, or, alternatively, writing an account of something that happened there. The exercise will likely help broaden your perspective.

最大的缘分

这 几年，缘字泛滥，见面就是缘。

在翠绿的伊犁河谷，一位哈萨克少女，高擎着马奶子酒说，尊贵的客人，世上最高最长远的缘分是什么呢？是吃啊！一生下来，婴儿就要吃。到不能吃的时候，缘分也就尽了。人们因吃而聚，因吃而离……

那一天，所有的味道，都被这句话漂白。

吃是笼罩天穹的巨伞。甚至从生命还没有诞生，我们就开始吃了。构成我们机体原初的那些物质：骨的钙，血的铁，瞳孔的胡萝卜素，头发的维生素原

123

B5，肌肉的纤维，脑神经的沟回……无一不是我们从大自然攫取来的。生命始自吃大自然，大自然是胚胎化缘的钵，这就是最洪荒的缘分啊。

出生后，我们开始吃母亲。乳汁是世界上最完整最易于消化吸收的养料，妈妈的胸怀，是我们赖以生存的谷仓，遮风雨的帐篷，温暖的火墙和日夜轰响的交响乐团（资料证明，婴儿在母亲的心跳声中，感觉最安宁。因为这声音的节奏，已融入孩子永恒的记忆）。因为吃与被吃，母与子，结成天下无与伦比的友谊。这种友谊被庄严地称为——母爱。

长大了，我们开始吃自己。养活你自己，几乎是进入成人界最显著的标志。填平空虚的胃，曾经是多少人惨淡经营的梦想。待统计到国计民生上，温饱解决了，我们就能进入小康，吃——此刻不仅仅是食物，更成了逾越文明纪录的标杆。吃是基础，吃是栋梁，有了吃，一个民族才能在世界的麦克风中有扩大的声音。没有吃，肚子咕咕叫的动静压倒一切，遑论其他！

夫妻走到一块儿，叫作从此在一个饭锅里搅马勺了。吃是男女长久的媒人和黏合剂。

普天之下，熙熙攘攘，多少酒肆饭楼，早茶晚宴，都是为吃聚在一处。古往今来，不知有多少大事在觥筹交错中议定，有多少金钱在餐桌下滚滚作响。

为了吃，人是残忍的，远古时曾尝遍了包括人自身在内的所有生物。进步了，不再吃人。科学了，不再吃有害健康的食物。但人的好吃仍是无与伦比，毒蛇有毒，拔了牙吃；河豚烈性，剥了内脏继续吃；珍禽异兽，都曾被人烹炸清炖，吃了南极吃北极，先是磷虾后是鲸……人是地球上能吃善吃的冠军，狮子老虎都得自叹弗如。

　　吃到遥远的地方，吃出奇异的境界，是人类永不磨灭的理想。所以人总想吃出地球去，吃到太空去，到另外的星球上找饭辙，这便是无限神往的明天了。

　　到什么也不想吃的时候，生命已到尾声，与这世界的缘分将尽了。所以能吃是最基本的缘分，切不可小觑。与"能吃"的可爱相比，功名利禄都是泔水。吃亦有道，须吃得聪明，吃得正大，吃得坦荡，吃的是自己双手挣来的清白，吃才是人间的幸福。

　　珍惜能吃的日子，珍惜一道举筷的亲人。珍惜畅饮的朋友，珍惜吃的智慧。敬畏热爱供给我们吃的原料、吃的场所、吃的机会、吃的概率的源头——大自然与母亲！

The Ultimate Bond

In recent years, the notion of "fate" — the force that brings people together — has been so overused that any situation, even a chance encounter with a total stranger, can somehow be described as "destined to happen."

Thus I found myself seated before a shepherd girl of Kazakh ethnicity in the verdant Ili River valley region, who, raising goblet filled with kumis, proclaimed her take on "fate": "My esteemed guests, what is the most powerful and enduring force that brings people together? Why, it's the urge to eat! This urge bonds us from birth till we stop eating for good. We take leave for the sake of food, and gather in joy to feast...."

Her remark that day gave a special twist to every flavour.

The urge to eat is pervasive and overwhelming. The ingestion of nutrients starts well before birth. The elements that make up our body — calcium for our bones, iron for our blood, carotene in the pupils of our eyes, Panthenol in our hair, and the building materials for our muscles and the grooves in our brain — all come from nature. The building materials for the embryo is provided via the placenta which itself needs feeding. Human life is dependent on ceaseless feeding upon inception. The urge to feed is primordial.

Upon birth, babies thrive on breast milk that has a perfect mix of nutrients, everything they need to grow, in a form most easily digested. Snug in the arms of the mother, the baby feels warm, assured, and protected. The mother's heartbeat provides the most soothing symphonic sounds. Research has found that the newborn is most peaceful when hearing the sound of mother's heartbeat that became familiar in utero. The mother-baby bond, without equal in all human relationships, starts with feeding; a remarkable relationship that has been sanctified as maternal love.

As we grow up, we learn to be autonomous in feeding. To be able to sustain yourself means coming of age. Having enough to eat was once a dream that many struggled to realize. As a measure of national development, having the whole population properly fed and clad is the defining feature of a moderately prosperous society. Food has become a yardstick and not allowing anyone to go hungry is a mark of the civilized society. Food consumption is the foundation of all things. A nation can only have its voice rightfully heard among nations, after it is properly fed. Short of which, all you can hear is nothing but the gurgling of the nation's famished stomach.

A married couple are proverbially "eating from the same pot." As it is often the case, the way to either a woman or man's heart is through their stomach.

In culinary establishments around the world, be it a fancy restaurant or humble eatery, people gather ostensibly to eat. Deals, great and greater, were made with avidity in the suitable atmosphere of wining and dining; money, in splendid amounts, changed hands under many a gastronomically enticing table.

Humans can also be barbarously brutal when it comes to eating. In ancient times, they tried all living things, even fellow humans. Civilization put a stop to ghastly man-eating-man. As science prevailed, people also refrained from eating foods detrimental to health. Yet human appetite is insatiable. Snakes can be venomous; yet this does not stop people eating them after plucking out their lethal fangs. The puffer fish can be deadly; yet men eat them after cleverly removing their innards. Deep-fried or tenderly steamed, any animal is game, from the most exotic beasts to the rarest birds. To push the boundaries, humans will stop at nothing; from gigantic whales to tiny krill and from pole to pole. As fierce predators, humans are at the pinnacle of the food chain, long putting king of the jungle to shame.

Humans will never cease in their search for the most elusive, exotic foodie experience. They even dream of extraterrestrial dining and interstellar dinner appointments. A feast on a far-flung planet could well be the next big thing for the celestially inclined.

Still, there will be a time when the appetite is finally gone and the end is near. Your bond with this world, no matter how predestined, will transpire. In this light, the urge to eat is the most fundamental — something not to be trivialized — and gastronomic satisfaction supreme, outweighing all worldly successes. There is also an ethical aspect to eating. Only by eating smart, eating right, and eating what you have rightfully earned, will eating be happiness itself.

Cherish the days when you enjoy eating; cherish the loved ones who share such enjoyment. Cherish the friends that drink to you; cherish the wits that you have for eating well. Above all, revere, love nature and our mother — the source of our nourishment, the provider of our sustenance, and the reason for our being.

提醒幸福

我们从小就习惯了在提醒中过日子。天气刚有一丝风吹草动，妈妈就说，别忘了多穿衣服。才结识了一个朋友，爸爸就说，小心他是个骗子。你取得了一点成功，还没容得乐出声来，所有关心你的人就一起说，别骄傲！你沉浸在欢乐中的时候，自己不停地对自己说，千万不可太高兴，苦难也许马上就要降临……我们已经习惯了在提醒中过日子，看得见的恐惧和看不见的恐惧始终像乌鸦盘旋在头顶。

在皓月当空的良宵，我们又会收到提醒，注意风暴。于是我们忽略了皎洁的月光，急急忙忙做好风暴来临前的一切准备。当我们大睁着眼睛枕戈待旦之时，风暴却像迟归的羊群，不知在哪里徘徊。当我们实在忍受不了等待灾难的煎熬时，我们甚至会祈盼风暴早些到来。

风暴终于姗姗地来了。我们怅然发现，所做的准备多半是没有用的。事先能够抵御的风险毕竟有限，世上无法预计的灾难却是无限的，战胜灾难靠的更多的是临门一脚，先前的惴惴不安帮不上忙。

当风暴的尾巴终于远去，我们守住家园，气还没有喘匀，新的提醒又响起来，我们又开始对未来充满恐惧和期待。

人生总是有灾难。其实大多数人早已练就了对灾难的从容，我们只是还没有学会灾难间隙的快活。我们太注重让自己警觉苦难，我们太忽视提醒幸福。

请从此注意幸福！

幸福也需要提醒吗？

提醒注意跌倒……提醒注意路滑……提醒受骗上当……提醒宠辱不惊……先哲们提醒了我们一万零一次，却不提醒我们幸福。

也许他们认为幸福不提醒也跑不了的。也许他们以为好的东西你自会珍惜，犯不上谆谆告诫。也许他们太崇尚血与火，觉得幸福无足挂齿。他们总是站在危崖上，指点我们逃离未来的苦难。但避去苦难之后是什么？

那就是幸福啊！

享受幸福是需要学习的，当幸福即将来临的时刻需要提醒。人可以自然而然地学会感官的享乐，却无法天生掌握幸福的韵律。灵魂的快意同器官的舒适像一对孪生兄弟，时而相傍相依，时而貌合神离。

幸福是一种心灵的震颤。它像会倾听音乐的耳朵一样，需要不断地训练。

简言之，幸福就是没有痛苦的时刻。它出现的频率并不像我们想象的那样少。人们常常只是在幸福的金马车已经驶过去很远后，才捡起地上的金鬃毛说，原来我见过它。

人们喜爱回味幸福的标本，却忽略幸福披着露水散发清香的时刻。那时候我们往往步履匆匆，瞻前顾后不知在忙着什么。

世上有预报台风的，有预报蝗虫的，有预报瘟疫的，有预报地震的，没有人预报幸福。其实幸福和世界万物一样，有它的征兆。

幸福常常是朦胧的，很有节制地向我们喷洒甘霖。你不要总希冀轰轰烈烈的幸福，它多半只是悄悄地扑面而来。你也不要企图把水龙头拧大，幸福会很快地流失，你需静静地以平和之心体验幸福的真谛。

幸福绝大多数是朴素的。它不会像信号弹似的在很高的天际闪烁红色的光芒，它披着本色外衣，温暖地包裹起我们。

幸福不喜欢喧嚣浮华，常常在暗淡中降临。贫困中相濡以沫的一块糕饼，患难中心心相印的一个眼神，父亲一次粗糙的抚摸，爱人一张温馨的字条……这都是千金难买的幸福啊，像一粒粒缀在旧绸子上的红宝石熠熠夺目。

幸福有时会同我们开一个玩笑，乔装打扮而来。机遇、友情、成功、团圆……它们都酷似幸福，但它们并不等同于幸福。幸福会借了它们的衣裙袅袅婷婷而来，走得近了，揭去帷幔，才发觉它有钢铁般的内核。幸福有时会很短暂，不像苦难似的笼罩天空。如果把人生的苦难和幸福分置天平两端，苦难体积庞大，幸福可能只是一块小小的矿石，但指针一定要向幸福这一侧倾斜，因为它是生命的黄金。

幸福有梯形的切面，它可以扩大也可以缩小，就看你是否珍惜。

我们要提高对于幸福的敏感，当它到来的时刻，激情地享受每一分钟。据科学家研究，有意注意的结果比无意的要好得多。

当春天来临的时候，我们要对自己说，这是春天啦！心里就会泛起茸茸的绿意。

幸福的时候，我们要对自己说，请记住这一刻！幸福就会长久地伴随我们。

那我们岂不是拥有了更多的幸福？

所以，丰收的季节先不要去想可能的灾年，我们还有漫长的冬季来考虑这件事。我们要和朋友们跳舞唱歌，渲染喜悦。既然种子已经回报了汗水，我们就有权沉浸在幸福中。不要管以后的风霜雨雪，让我们先把麦子磨成面粉，烘一个香喷喷的面包。

所以，当我们从天涯海角相聚在一起的时候，请不要踌躇片刻后的别离。在今后漫长的岁月里，有无数孤寂的夜晚可以独自品尝愁绪。现在的每一分钟，都让它像纯净的酒精，燃烧成幸福的淡蓝色火焰，不留一丝渣滓。让我们一起举杯，说：我们幸福。

所以，当我们守候在年迈的父母膝下时，哪怕他们鬓发苍苍，哪怕他们垂垂老矣，你都要有勇气对自己说：我很幸福。因为天地无常，总有一天你会失去他们，会无限追悔此刻的时光。

幸福并不与财富、地位、声望、婚姻同步，这只是你心灵的感觉。

所以，当我们一无所有的时候，我们也能够说：我很幸福。因为我们还有健康的身体。当我们不再享有健康的时候，那些最勇敢的人依然可以微笑着说：我很幸福，因为我还有一颗健康的心。甚至当我们连心也不再存在的时候，那些人类最优秀的分子仍旧可以对宇宙大声说：我很幸福，因为我曾经生活过。

常常提醒自己注意幸福，就像在寒冷的日子里经常看看太阳，心就不知不觉暖洋洋、亮光光。

Celebrate Happiness

We have become accustomed to living our lives with endless reminders since childhood. At the slightest hint of autumn, you are urged by your mom to put on layers. Hardly have you started going out with someone when your dad cautions you — Be wary of any possible cheat. When you have achieved a modicum of success, you are promptly advised in unison by all who care about you — Rest not on your laurels, before you have barely congratulated yourself. Thus, in your moments of bliss, you skittishly remind yourself not to be overjoyed, for hardship may lurk around the corner. We take such reminders as a given, letting omens of peril hover over our head, as it were, like dark, imaginary ravens.

On a beautiful moonlit night, we can be warned of an impending storm. We scamper off to get prepared, oblivious to the blessed moonlight. As we wait with rounded eyes for the imminent gloom, the storm wanders in its path like lost sheep. With the weight of anxiety unbearable, we even start to pray for its imminent arrival.

When the storm finally hits, we find to our chagrin much of our preparedness has come to naught. With infinite possibilities for calamities in the world, the measures we can take to pre-empt them are pitifully finite. Being on pins and needles all day does little good. Luck aside, it is the prompt, effective actions that will save our skin at the end of the day.

As the storm tapers off, with our homes intact, we are reminded of possible new dangers; being seized with fear and anxiety all over again, barely have we been able to breathe easily.

We cannot go through life without mishaps. Most of us have learned to take them in stride. We are yet to learn to be happy in the intervals. We are so focused on averting possible suffering that we often fail to count our blessings.

Pay attention to happiness from now on.

Yet, do we need such a reminder?

With the words of our wise elders ringing in our ears, we have been urged umpteen times to mind our steps; to not slip and fall as we walk; to be alert to scams; to be inured to either favour or humiliation... But never once were we urged to be happy.

Perhaps to them, happiness befalls when it does, regardless of us being reminded or otherwise. Perhaps they believed we would cherish our blessings without their urging. Perhaps they valued fortitude under life's trials and misfortune so highly that they believed happiness was not worth a whistle. They precipitously pointed us to the path out of our misery. Yet what happens afterwards?

Why, it is happiness!

We all need to learn to enjoy happiness. We also need a prompt, a gentle tug, when it befalls. We are naturally inclined to revel in sensory delights; yet our appreciation of happiness has to be learned. What pleases our soul and body can be the same or different, depending on the given circumstances and time.

Happiness makes our heart sing, like music to the practiced ear. Its appreciation requires training and honing.

Happiness is not some kind of rare occurrence, as elusive as we might have imagined. It can simply be the absence of suffering. People often come to appreciate how blessed they are after the fact, seeing it in the golden hues of nostalgia; a passing train fading into the sunset.

We like to wax nostalgic on happy times of yore while being oblivious to the here and now. We rush through life in such haste; busy and ever anxious, for fear of missing the train.

We can predict a plethora of natural events, from typhoon, locust plagues, and endemic diseases to earthquakes. We are yet to have the knack to forecast happiness. Yet, like everything else in this world, happiness also gives early signs.

The feeling of happiness can often be subtle, more like a mist hugging the valley wall than a drizzle. Happiness is not always a rousing state of blissfulness. You feel the glow, more often than not, in your hours of peace and quiet contentment. Never overdo your enjoyment, for its will only hasten its dissipation.

Happiness most often finds expression in simplicity. It never proclaims its onset, as it were, with a signal flare blazing bright and high, and seen miles away. It is more like a plain, warm blanket that you snuggle under on a cold night.

Happiness favours not the rowdy reveller; befalling more often in the gloom of twilight. Happiness is a morsel of flatbread shared between two impoverished, loving souls. It is in the look of understanding and support cast your way when you are down on your luck. It is the pat on the back by your father with his calloused hand. It is a loving note scribbled by your partner... Such is happiness a thousand taels of gold will not buy; like rubies set in a plain, threadbare tapestry, radiant still.

Happiness sometimes plays deceptive tricks on us, hidden behind the veil of a fortuitous opportunity, companionship, worldly success, or reunion that may seem to be, yet not exactly, happiness. Upon examination, what lies beneath is a steely core. Unlike suffering that is often pervasive and interminable, and depressive like the leaden sky, happiness is intense and metamorphic, like a chunk of mineral. If misery and happiness were put on a scale, the former being loose and bulky, while the latter gold — tilting the scale in its favour.

Happiness is never static; capable of expanding or contracting; depending on how much we cherish it.

We should more keenly feel happiness, relishing every minute of its fleeting existence. Research has shown keen attention produces far better enjoyment.

As spring arrives, let us sing out, Spring is here! Hardly

are those words out when our heart has brimmed with verdant joy.

Basking in the glow of happiness, we should urge ourselves, Remember such moments! The blissfulness will stay and be cherished by us for a long time to come.

In so doing, we can surely build a greater store of happiness for our life, wouldn't you say?

Thus, let us joyfully celebrate our harvest and, while we are at it, enjoy and not worry about future calamities. We will have the whole winter to brood over such possibilities. Let us celebrate, with singing and dancing, the reward we rightly deserve. Be it wind or snow tomorrow, for now let us break bread, hot from oven and a slice of heaven; full of freshly harvested, natural goodness.

Thus, as we are rejoined with friends from afar, we should not slip into forlorn gloom over inevitable leave-taking. We will have endless lonesome nights for melancholy and nostalgia later. Let us enjoy our camaraderie now; let our joy glow, brightly like a flame, pure and blue. Let us raise a rousing cheer, *"We are happy as the day is long!"*

As we take care of our aging parents, we shall have courage enough to say we are blessed, even though the flame of their life is starting to flicker. Or else we will be left with forlorn regret after we lose them one day, and all that goes with it, given the transient nature of life.

Happiness is not synonymous to wealth, station, fame and fortuitous wedlock; it is a blessed state of your soul.

We can be happy even when we have nothing to our name, for we have good health. Even when we suffer poor health, the brave among us still feel happy, for they are blessed with a good heart. When our heart goes at last, the finest of us claim utmost happiness for having truly lived.

Remind yourself often to cherish your happiness; let your heart be warmed by its radiant glow; like the glorious sun, a toasty fire, on a day of wintry gale.

带白蘑菇回家

妈妈爱吃蘑菇。

我到青海出差，在幽蓝的天穹与黛绿的草原之间，我见到点点闪烁的白星。

那不是星星，是草原上的白蘑菇。

路旁有三三两两的藏族同胞，坐在五颜六色的口袋中间，仰着褐色的面庞，向经过的汽车微笑。袋子口，颤巍巍地露出花蕾般的白蘑菇。

从鸟岛返回的途中，我买了一袋白蘑菇，预备两天后坐火车带回北京。

回到宾馆，铺下一张报纸，将蘑菇一柄柄小伞朝天，摆在地毯上，一如它们生长在草原时的模样。

服务员进来打扫卫生，细细的眉头皱了起来。我忙说："我要把它们带回去送给妈妈。"服务员就暖暖地笑了，说："您必须把蘑菇翻个身，让菌根朝上，不然蘑菇会烂的。草原上的白蘑菇最难保存。"

听了服务员的话，我就让白蘑菇趴在地上，好像晒太阳的小胖孩儿，温润而圆滑地裸露在空气中。

上火车的日子到了。服务员帮我找来一个小纸箱，用剪刀戳了许多梅花形的小洞，把白蘑菇妥妥地安放进去。原先的报纸上印了一排排圆环，好像淡淡的墨色的图章。我吓了一跳，说："是不是白蘑菇腐坏了？"服务员说："别怕。新鲜的白蘑菇的汁液就是黑的。"

进了卧铺车厢，我小心翼翼地把纸箱塞在床下。对面一位青海大汉说："箱子上捅了这么多洞，想必带的是活物了。小鸡？小鸭？怎么听不见叫？天气太热，可别憋死了。"

我说："带的是草原上的白蘑菇，送给妈妈。"

他轻轻地重复："哦，妈妈……"好像这个词语对他已十分陌生。半晌后他才接着说，"只是你这样的带法，到不了兰州，蘑菇就得烂成污水。"

我大惊失色，说："那可怎么办？"

他说:"你在卧铺下面铺开几张纸,把蘑菇晾开,保持它的通风。"

我依法处置,摆了一床底的蘑菇。每日数次拨弄,好像育秧的老农。蘑菇们平安地穿兰州,越宝鸡,抵西安,直逼郑州……不料中原地带,酷热无比,车厢内郁闷如桑拿浴池,令人窒息。青海大汉不放心地蹲下检查,突然叫道:"快想办法!蘑菇表面已生出白膜,再捂下去就不能吃了!"

在蒸笼般的火车里,还有什么办法可想?我束手无策。

大汉二话不说,把我的白蘑菇重新装进浑身是洞的纸箱。我说:"这不是更糟了?"他并不解释,三下五除二,把卧铺小茶几上的水杯、食品拢成一堆,对周围的人说:"烦请各位把自家的东西,拿到别处去放。腾出这张小桌,来放小箱子。箱子里装的是咱青海湖的白蘑菇,她要带回北京给妈妈。我们把窗户开大,让风不停地灌进箱子,蘑菇就坏不了啦。大家帮帮忙,我们都有妈妈。"

人们无声地把面包、咸鸭蛋和可乐瓶子拿走,为我腾出一方洁净的桌面。

风呼啸着。郑州的风、安阳的风、石家庄的风……接连不断，穿箱而过，白蘑菇黑色的血液渐渐被蒸发了，烘成干燥的标本。

青海大汉坐在窗口迎风的一面，疾风把他的头发卷得乱如蒿草，无数灰屑敷在他铁棠色的脸上，犹如漫天抛撒的芝麻。若不是为了这一箱蘑菇，玻璃窗原不必开得这样大。我几次歉意地说同他换换位子，他却一摆手说："草原上的风比这还大。"

终于，北京到了。我拎起蘑菇箱子同车友们告别，对大家说："我代表自己和妈妈谢谢你们！"

大家说："你快回家去看妈妈吧。"

由于路上蒸发了水分，白蘑菇比以前轻了许多。我走得很快，就要出站台的时候，青海大汉追上我，说："有一件很要紧的事，忘了同你交代——白蘑菇炖鸡最鲜。"

妈妈喝着鸡汤说："青海的白蘑菇味道真好！"

Meadow Mushrooms from Afar

My mother loves mushrooms.

On a trip to Qinghai, I was struck by the verdant rolling grassland dotted with tiny white specks, like stars set in a deep blue sky.

They were of course not stars, but meadow mushrooms that had come out in force. Tibetans with bagfuls of them could be seen sitting on the roadside in twos and threes, with smiles on their tawny faces. The fluffy caps peeked out the multi-coloured bags, quivering in the wind like flower buds as vehicles rumbled past.

Returning from a visit to the Bird Island on Qinghai Lake,

I bought a bagful of the meadow mushrooms, planning to take them back to Beijing two days later.

Back in the hotel room, I placed all the mushrooms on a sheet of newspaper with their caps turned upward just as they grew in the field.

Seeing this, the chambermaid who came in to clean the room furrowed her thin eyebrows. I hastened to explain, "I will be taking them home for my mother." "Oh, you have to turn their stems upward," she said with a warm smile, "or they will wither and rot fast. The meadow mushrooms are the toughest to keep."

Heeding her advice, I flipped all the mushrooms. Now with their stems upward, they each looked smooth and plump, like chubby little babies, naked in airy sunlight.

As the day for my departure came, the chambermaid found me a small cardboard box. The mushrooms were all placed snugly and the box had tiny petal-shaped holes punched with a pair of scissors to let in air. Neat rows of stains like inky stamp marks were left on the newspaper. I was startled, "Have they gone bad?" "No," the girl assured me, "it's normal for them to leave that kind of stains."

After I had boarded the train, I carefully tucked the box under my berth. A stocky local man sitting on the opposite berth said, "So many holes punched in the box! Must be something alive. Chicks or ducklings, if I may ask? Why aren't they making any noises? You'd better make sure they are okay on such a hot day."

"They are mushrooms for my mother," I said.

"Oh, for your mother..." he muttered, little awkwardly as if the last word were a little strange to him. He continued after a pause, "The way you carry them, they'd all spoil before you reach Lanzhou."

I panicked, "What should I do?"

"Spread them out on a few sheets of paper under your berth," he said. "They need to be kept in an airy place."

I spread the mushrooms out, as told, across the floor underneath my berth, turning them over a couple of times during the day like an old farmer fussing over seedlings. The mushrooms passed Lanzhou, Baoji, and Xi'an safe and sound before reaching Zhengzhou. It was swelteringly hot as the train reached the central plains and the compartment was like a sauna house. The Qinghai man crouched down for a closer look at the mushrooms before he blurted out, "Do something now! They are getting mouldy. They'd spoil soon if left like this."

What can I do in this sweltering heat? I felt helpless.

Without a word, the Qinghai man put all the mushrooms back into the box. "Will it make it worse?" I muttered. He didn't reply but quickly pushed the mugs and snacks on the small table together, before asking the other passengers, "Can you all put away your stuff to make space for this box? These are meadow mushrooms from Qinghai. She is taking them back to Beijing for her mother. We all know what this means. Everybody please! We will lift the window up for some air so the mushrooms won't rot."

Silently, people moved away their stuff —
bread buns, salted duck eggs and cola bottles —
from the small table to make room for me.

Wind gushed in. Winds of Zhengzhou,
Anyang, and Shijiazhuang... winds of one town
after another... flowed through the box. The wilting
mushrooms began to lose their dark moisture, and
eventually became air-dried specimens.

The Qinghai man was in a forward-facing
berth and the wind tousled his hair, turning it
into a rough tangle. Dust and grime, as if tossed
sesame, clung to his tawny, wind-beaten face.
If not for my box of mushrooms, the window
wouldn't have to be lifted up like this. I felt sorry
and offered to switch berths with him a couple of
times. He simply waved it off, saying "The wind on
the plateau is far worse than this."

At long last, we reached Beijing. Picking up

my box of mushrooms, I bid farewell to my fellow travellers, "Thanks on behalf of my mother and I myself!"

Everyone replied, "Have a great visit with your mother."

As the mushrooms had dried out, the box was much lighter. I walked briskly toward the station exit, before the Qinghai man caught up with me, "I forgot to mention a very important thing — meadow mushroom cooked in chicken broth is the most delicious."

Sipping her soup, my mother echoed, "The mushroom from Qinghai tastes so good!"

盲人看

每逢放学的时候，附近的那所小学，就有稠厚的人群，糊在铁门前，好似风暴前的蚁穴，那是家长等着接各自的孩童回家。

在远离人群的地方，有个人倚着毛白杨，悄无声息地站着，从不张望校门口。直到有一个孩子飞快地跑过来，拉着他说，爸，咱们回家。他把左手交给孩子，右手拄起盲杖，一同横穿马路。

多年前，这盲人常蹲在路边，用二胡奏很哀伤的曲调。他技艺不好，琴也质劣，音符断断续续地抽噎，叫人听了只想快快远离。他面前盛着零碎钱的破罐头盒，永远看得到锈蚀的罐底。我偶尔放一点钱进去，也是堵着耳朵近前。

后来，他摆了一个小摊子，卖点手绢袜子什么的，生意很淡。一天晚上，我一下公共汽车，黑寂就包抄而来。原来这一片突然停电，连路灯都灭了。只有电线杆旁，一束光柱如食指捅破星天。靠拢后才见是那盲人打了手电，在卖蜡烛、火柴，价格很便宜，我赶紧买了一份，喜滋滋地觉着给亲人带回了光明。

之后的某个白日，我又在路旁看到盲人，就气哼哼地走过去，说，你不能趁着停电，发这种不义之财啊。那天你卖的蜡烛，算什么货色啊？蜡烛油四下流，烫了我的手。烛捻一点也不亮，小得像个萤火虫尾巴。

他愣愣地把塌陷的眼窝对着我，半天才说，对不住，我……不知道……蜡烛的光……该有多大。萤火虫的尾巴……是多亮。那天听说停电，就赶紧批了蜡烛来卖。我只知道……黑了，难受。

我呆住了。那个漆黑的夜晚，即便烛火如豆，还是比完全的黑暗好了不知几多。一个盲人在为明眼人操心，我还不分青红皂白地指责他，我好悔。

后来，我很长时间没到他的摊子买东西。确信他把我的声音忘掉之后，有一天，我买了一堆杂物，然后放下了五十块钱，对盲人说，不必找了。我抱着那些东西，走了没几步，被他叫住了，大姐，你给我的是多少钱啊？

我说，是五十元。

他说，我从来没拿过这么大的票子。

见他先是平着指肚，后是立起掌根，反复摩挲钞票的正反面。

我说，这钱是真的，您放心。

他笑笑说，我从来没收到过假币。谁要是欺负一个盲人，他的心先就瞎了。我只是不能收您这么多的钱，我是在做买卖啊。

我知道自己又一次错了。

不知他在哪里学了按摩，经济上渐渐地有了起色，从乡下找了一个盲眼的姑娘成了亲。一天，我到公园去，忽然看到他们夫妻相跟着，沿着花径在走。四周湖光山色美若仙境，我想，这对他们来讲，真是一种残酷。

闪过他们身旁的时候，听到盲夫有些炫耀地问，怎么样？我领你来这儿，景色不错吧？好好看看吧。

盲妻不服气地说，好像你看过似的。

盲夫很肯定地说，我看过，常来看的。

听一个盲人连连响亮地说出"看"这个词，叫人顿生悲凉，也觉出一些滑稽。

盲妻反唇相讥道，介绍人不是说你胎里瞎吗？啥时看到这里好景色呢？

盲夫说，别人用眼看，咱可以用心看，用耳朵看，用手看，用鼻子看……加起来一点不比别人少啊。

那一瞬，我凛然一惊。

世上有很多东西，看了如同未看，我们眼在神不在。记住并真正懂得的东西，必得被心房茧住啊。

后来盲夫妇有了果实，一个瞳仁亮如秋水的男孩。他渐渐长大，上了小学，盲人便天天接送。

起初那孩童躲在盲人背后，跟着杖子走，慢慢地胆子壮了，绿灯一亮，就跳着要越过去。父亲总是死死拽住他，用盲杖戳着柏油路说，让我再听听，近处没有车轮声，我们才可动……

终有一天，孩子对父亲讲，爸，我给你带路吧。他拉起父亲，东张西望，然后一蹦一跳地越过地上的斑马线。于是盲人第一次提起他的盲杖，跟着目光如炬的孩子，无所顾忌地前行，脚步抬得高高的，轻捷如飞。

孩子越来越大了，当明眼人都不再接送这么高的孩子时，盲人依旧每天倚在校旁的杨树下，等待着。

What Do the Blind See?

There was always a throng in front of the elementary school near my home when it was about to let out. Clinging to the metal gate, restless like a swarm of ants before a looming storm, they were parents waiting to pick up their kids.

Far from this crowd, a man stood quietly, leaning against a poplar and never casting a glance in the direction of the school gate. He waited till a boy ran up to and tugged at him, saying, "Dad, let's go home!" He would place his left hand in the child's and, with a cane in his right, start crossing the street.

I had first seen this blind man years earlier. He'd often

squat on the pavement, playing sad tunes on his erhu. He didn't play well and his instrument shabby. The tunes were so woeful that passersby would hurry past him as fast as they could. The little tin in front of him was almost always empty, showing its rusty bottom. I'd drop a few coins occasionally, covering my ears as I did that.

Later, he became a hawker with a stand selling handkerchiefs and socks; yet hardly getting any customers. Returning home one evening, I was engulfed by darkness as I got off the bus. There was a power outage in the district and the street was pitch dark, except for a beam of light next to a utility pole, shooting upward as if a luminous finger pointing at the starry sky. It was the blind man's torch — he was selling candles and matches on the cheap. I bought a pack of candles, smug about being able to bring light to folks groping in the dark at home.

A few days later, as I saw the man in the street again, I walked over, huffing and puffing.

"How could you take advantage of the blackout and

swindle people?" I seethed. "What lousy candles you were selling the other day! My hand got burned by the splattering wax. The wicker was so small that the flame was no more than a firefly!"

He looked dumbstruck, turning his face, with its sunken eye sockets, toward me.

"I am sorry," he muttered after a long moment. "I … didn't know what a candle's flame should be like … how bright a firefly can look. After I was told about the power outage, I bought the candles from a wholesaler. I knew how horrible it is to be in the dark."

I was stunned. Indeed, on that night of blackout, having the feeble light of a bean-sized flame was still better than in complete darkness. I felt ashamed of blindly blaming a blind man who was thoughtful of the seeing.

I avoided patronizing his stand for a long while, until I was sure that he must have forgotten my voice. Then one day, after picking up a pile of stuff from his stand, I put down a fifty-yuan bill, telling him to keep the change. Hardly had I walked a few steps away when he called out, "Ma'am, how much did you pay me?"

"Fifty yuan," I said.

"I have never touched such a large bill," he said, as he felt both sides of the banknote, first with the balls of the fingers and then his palm.

"It is authentic," I assured him.

"I have never been given fake money," he said with a smile. "Anyone trying to cheat the blind would be rotten at heart. I just can't take this much money from you. I am doing honest business, not panhandling."

I knew then I had wronged him again.

Then, he learned to practice massage therapy and his straitened circumstances slowly improved. He married a blind girl from the country. One day, I saw the couple in the park, one following the other, down a small path by the sparkling green lake against the backdrop of distant hills. It was kind of cruel to the couple, I thought, who couldn't see such a picture-perfect landscape.

As they passed by, I overheard the man saying showily, "How do you like it? You don't regret having me take you here, do you? Such beautiful scenes! Take a good look!"

"You sounded as if you have seen them!" his wife quipped, unimpressed.

"Indeed I have," the man retorted. "I came here often to look at them."

Hearing the man talking about looking and seeing, I couldn't help feeling a twinge of sadness, as well as irony.

"Weren't you born blind?" his wife shot back. "That's what the matchmaker said. When did you actually see the pretty sceneries here?"

"Well, others see with their eyes," the blind man offered, "and we see with our heart, our ear, our hand, and our nose…. With all these senses together, we are at no disadvantage at all."

His words tore at my heartstrings. Too often, we find ourselves looking but not seeing, when our heart just isn't in it. You only truly appreciate and commit to your memory what is dear to your heart.

Still later, the couple had a son, with sparkling, bright eyes. As he grew up and started school, the blind man would walk him to, and pick him up from, school every day.

At first, the boy would always follow after the man walking with his stick. In time, he became bolder and wanted to rush as the light turned green. His father would grab him by the arm and tapped the asphalt with his cane, saying, "Let's listen first to make sure no vehicles are coming, and then cross the street."

Eventually, the boy declared one day, "Dad, let me walk you across the street." He took his father's hand and looked to left and then right before moving with bouncy steps through zebra crossing. For the first time ever, the man held his cane off the ground and followed the sharp-eyed boy, striding across the street.

As the boy grew up and other parents had long stopped walking their kids to and picking them up after school, the blind man could still be seen waiting by the lone poplar outside the school gate day in, day out, every day without fail.

可否让我陪你哭泣

哭泣是一种本能，古代人却害怕它。因为哭泣代表着一种极端状况的发生，人们本能地回避。

我说过，自己在妇产科工作时经手接生过很多婴儿。假如是顺产的孩子，他们降生后的第一反应就是号啕大哭。其实，这种音响的本质不应该被称为"哭"，他们从温暖的子宫降生到外界，感受到了寒冷，再加上压力骤然解除，肺部扩张，强力地吸入空气，就发出了人们称为"哭喊"的声音。实话实说，这种啼哭并不哀伤，只是一种体操。

我觉得真正区分哭泣的哀伤程度的，是眼泪。

其实哭是可以分成两种的，流泪的和不流泪的。没有眼泪的哭泣，更多的是压抑。只有那种泪流汹涌、滴泪沾襟的哭泣，才有更大的宣泄和排解压力的作用。

洋葱也会让我们流泪，不过这种泪只是一些成分简单的水分。而人们因为悲伤流出的泪，含有大量的激素。

悲伤或愤怒的眼泪包含着脑啡肽，是大脑缓解疼痛的溶解剂。哭泣触动了分泌与释放激素的化学物质，排出了造成压力的激素。这是一种宝贵的外分泌过程。我们要找回哭泣的能量，好好利用这个武器。眼泪能排毒啊。

聆听别人的痛楚，常常让我们觉得难以忍受。

有一阵子，我的诊所里接二连三地来了一些丧失亲人、需做悲伤治疗的人。他们之中少数人是无声地哭泣，让眼泪顺着面颊汹涌而下。大部分人会撕心裂肺地痛哭，几乎声震寰宇。

诊所的工作人员说，她在外面都听得到声如裂帛般的哭声，我近在咫尺洗耳恭听，如何受得了呢！

我说，事实上并没有你想象的那样难挨。天下之大，其实是难以找到可以放声一哭的地方。从这个角度来说，他或她，能够让我陪伴着痛哭，是给予我极大的信任啊。

在朋友的交往中，也常有这种情境。

如果你觉得不可忍受，多半是因为这痛苦也正是你掩藏的创口。别人的叙述，像一柄挖掘的铲，让你的陈血也开始喷溅。这种时刻，你不要轻易放过。如果你不能倾听，可以躲开，但要讲清自己不是厌倦，而是无力支撑。我相信真正的朋友会理解这一点的。如果不能理解，也就不可久交了。

但你歇息下来的时候，不要轻易放过那稍纵即逝的痛楚。我猜，身体已经习惯于包裹最深的弹片，轻易不愿触动。不过还是要把它挖出来，虽然一段时间内会血流不止，不过伤口终将愈合，如果一直遮掩着，倒有可能导致精神的败血症。

Sharing Grief

Crying is a human instinct. Yet, humans in ancient times were fearful of, and averse to, crying, for it meant something extreme had happened.

When working at one time in the obstetrics and gynaecology department of a hospital, I helped deliver many babies. The first reflex of newborns right after natural birth is crying. However, such a physical reaction is different from crying in response to an emotional state. A baby's first cry expands and fills up its lungs and helps its to breathe on its own, as it is being turned out into a strange, cold world, with all the pressure it experienced in the snug, warm womb suddenly gone. In fact, such crying is by no means sad, but rather a set of physical reflexes. It is the tear that really tells how sad someone's crying is.

Crying can be with or without tears. Tearless sobbing usually indicates suppression of emotional pain. Only crying with abandon, not holding back tears, can provide catharsis and better relieve stress.

Onions make our eyes water; yet such watery tears are mostly just water, while tears of sadness contain greater quantities of hormones. Tears caused by sorrow or anger contain encephalin which occurs in the brain and has analgesic properties. Crying stimulates the release of such brain chemicals and sheds hormones that cause stress. This is an important exocrine process wherein lies the healing power of crying. We should all make better use of such power. After all, tears help us get rid of toxins and recover from emotional distress.

Lending an ear to others in pain, we may often find it beyond what we can bear.

At one time, I was seeing a string of visitors at my clinic who had lost loved ones and needed grief counselling. A few of them cried silently with unstoppable tears rolling down their cheeks, while others wailed and howled in a thunderous, excruciating manner.

My staff at the clinic would say, "How could you even bear their wailing in such proximity? It was ear-splitting even to us outside the room."

"It was not as bad as you think," I would reply. "Indeed, it can be tough to find somewhere in the whole wide world where you could have a good cry. It shows their utmost trust that they allowed me to be in their presence when they cried in such pain."

The same holds true for our friends.

If you find their crying unbearable, it is often because their grief touches a hidden wound in you. Their recounting may poke your old wound like a lancet and make it bleed again.

You should not let such moments pass in vain. If you cannot bear listening any more, you can make yourself scarce, making it clear, however, that you are doing this not out of disdain, but because the the grief is beyond what you can bear. Without doubt, your friends will understand. Otherwise, it is not a friendship that will endure.

Yet, in your moment of quietness, contemplate that feeling of pain and don't let it slip away too soon. The human body, with a shrapnel lodged and encysted inside, will resist its being stirred. So do we, emotionally, with our pain deep inside. Yet, we need to clearly define and dislodge it, even though it will cause the old wound to bleed again, before it is finally healed; for left untouched, it may well lead to "sepsis," emotional and physiological.

宁静有一种特殊的力量

宁静有一种特殊的力量，就是不管外界怎样变化无常，都能让你的躯体自在平和。就像一艘在狂风巨浪中保持着稳定的船，你难道不惊异于它锚链的深度和船体的坚固吗？

我喜欢宁静的风景和宁静的人，这使我怡然。我的老师林教授曾经帮我分析过这种爱好的形成。她说，你是不是因为在西藏待得太久了，雪山和冰峰静止不动，久而久之，也就养成了你寂静的性格？

我承认她说得有道理。不过，我的幼儿园老师曾说过，我从小就是一个安静的孩子。

真的是这样吗？我不知道。我知道自己的心里常常翻涌着惊涛骇浪。我知道这是我必须经历的，并不害怕。但我不会很激烈地把它表达出来，我觉得有一些事情要出现，就让它出现好了。我不能阻止它们，但可以平静地面对它们。

　　我在西藏的高原上，看到过这个世界最为纯净的水。它们来自亿万年前的冰川。我常常站立在波涛翻卷的狮泉河边发呆，心想，水的力量和生命是多么伟大啊。它们历经沧桑，仍然珠圆玉润，没有一丝疲惫和倦怠。看不到些许的伤痕，更没有皱纹和白发，永远年轻地喧嚣着，如同新生的那一刹那。

　　我原来是很敬佩山的，但和水相比，山的自我修复能力要差很多，它们只能不由自主地风化下去，不可复原。山只能沿着一条没有回头的路，照直地走下去，大块的岩石崩塌，化为细碎的沙砾，然后继续颓弱，变作齑粉样的泥沙，再衰变为黄土……

　　人的心，还是像水吧。可以受伤，但永远有痊愈的力量。在大自然面前，人什么都无须保留，只需堂堂正正即可。

The Power of Silence

Silence has a special power of its own.

That is to say that, however bizarre the changes going on around you, you keep your cool, like a boat gliding calmly through tumultuous waters. Won't you be struck by the depth of the anchor and the sturdiness of the boat?

I myself prefer quiet scenes and placid people. They make me feel at ease. Professor Lin, my teacher, had pointed out for me the source of this propensity to quietness. She had said: "Don't you think you may have been too long in Tibet? Facing the snowy mountains and the icy peaks from day to day? Silent and unmoving! Over time, they creep upon you and affect your character."

She has a case, I acknowledge. My kindergarten teacher used to say that I had been a quiet little girl from the start. Is that true? I am not sure. But it is a fact that my heart is often racked with upheavals, and I have no fear. I accept these upheavals as something that I must go through. I cannot stop these upheavals, but I can face them calmly.

Up on the heights of Tibet, I had seen the clearest water in the world. They used to be icicles from eons of years ago. I would often stand on the banks of the tumultuous Lion Spring River, musing on the power and vitality of water. Having gone through so many ups and downs, water is still full of their original vitality and sparkle with no signs of fatigue, no white hairs, and even less signs of damage, keeping up its youthful roar, like the day they were born.

I had always maintained a reverence for mountains, but they stand no comparison with water in the ability for self-repair. Helpless, they wither away as time goes by and cannot be restored. Mountains have no choice but to follow a path, with no turning back. Rocks fall apart, turning into scattered sand, deteriorating into dust, ending up as yellow earth.

Man's heart, hopefully, is more like water. It can be hurt, but it can also self-repair. Face to face with nature, man need not hoard.

All it takes is to be a man of honour.